GREENER DATA

Actionable Insights from Industry Leaders

JAYMIE SCOTTO AND ASSOCIATES (JSA)

ISBN: 979-8-9856016-3-3

ISBN: 979-8-9856016-4-0

Contents

Introduction

Jaymie Scotto Cutaia

Two words: Ava Capri. That's the name of my ultimate 'spiritual why', my legacy, my daughter. She is the reason why I write this-the reason for asking these amazing authors to contribute a chapter. And it's because I owe her. I owe her an Earth where she can breathe, where she can run, giggle, collect seashells, turn mud into mud pies as the Pacific waves come up and play along her ankles.

I have carried her through a pandemic, given birth to her in a bathtub, watched her take her first breaths, open her large blue-gray eyes, and sip in the world around her. And now I look down, and see a sweet child, eyes like globes, staring back wondrously.

As I hold her in my arms, I imagine her as a future astronaut who will have to explore space and planets for survival, as we, our generation, lost the greatest battle humanity forgot to fight: the battle for a Greener Earth.

Even as we commit these words to paper, like a little time capsule, the news blares from the nearby TV. Russia invades Ukraine. Overnight, humans have once again turned on themselves, brothers fighting brothers, senseless killings, refugees fleeing, babies in arms, all those babies looking just like Ava, and mothers everywhere not understanding the madness that can come from trying to redraw lines on maps in a relentless pursuit to control others. Why should a corrupt few have the power to drive our children to kill or flee?

And haven't we as humans changed? Our sensibilities? Our ability to share and listen to one another across global social platforms? Hasn't this sharing shown us that we are indeed connected and more the same than different?

Just days before, I was watching Ava in the park, taking turns on a swing with another toddler, thinking the pandemic is lessening its grip on us now. We can focus on healing together, sharing again. People letting other people in once more.

How did we pivot so drastically overnight? Killing one another. Fearing one another.

Aren't we past seeing each other as 'others' instead of as one?

And why have we given up on Earth? Billionaires are spending their valuable resources on building their own spaceships, with a limited number of seats. What are they really telling us? Is it truly too late?

A few months back, I read a statistic that forever changed me. A recent International Energy Agency (IEA) report stated that *approximately 2.5% of global energy is consumed by data centers and data networks, and this number is expected to quickly rise, with global energy used by data centers alone to increase to 8-10% by 2030.* That's a staggering number and a staggering increase. And as a person who has spent her career promoting data centers and telecom networks, I felt directly responsible.

Perhaps my younger self would have responded differently, shrugged it off. But after just delivering a child, the predictions of this report leapt off the page and stood in sharp focus in front of me, crept inside my bones, rattled in my brain when I tried to sleep. These numbers became minutes ticking down. A last breath of my child or her children, a promise broken. And no question, this was done on my watch.

'Ava' means life. And yet I am giving her life in an unsustainable climate; I am giving her a planet in crisis.

I have spent my career promoting technology to connect

humans, creating opportunities for communication, sharing and collaborating- but at the expense of carbon emissions that are slowly suffocating the Earth.

This guilt, sadness, hurt had me asking once again, what is it that I believe in? I have faith—faith in a Greater Purpose—from a Greater Power—and faith that Ava is meant for more.

Previously in my life, my most difficult challenges turned into solutions because of technology, innovation, and people coming together to affect change. Can the same equation be applied to this planet's crisis?

I knew I didn't have the answers, but I had friends who were each tackling this great challenge in their own companies and countries.

As the head of a public relations agency catering to the data center and telecom industry, I found myself in a unique position where I was hearing multiple smart approaches, but walled off from other like-minded people, ideas and innovations. What if we could break down our silos, our company lines, our country boundaries, and instead be citizens of Earth, sharing our approaches, for others to seek inspiration and commit to getting greener in their own businesses, facilities and/or technologies? Out of this question, the idea for *Greener Data* was born.

What if a multi-author book could become the beginning of real change. What if we could turn these multiple, individual ideas into a collective movement?

As the industry responsible for at minimum 2.5% of global energy consumption, that means we can quickly come together and solve for the resulting global carbon emissions directly, and ideally write the prescription for others to reduce their carbon footprints, in their industries, in their companies, with their part-ners, and together, we can provide a real legacy to our children.

On a late night in November 2021, when the pandemic was still raging with threats of a new variant on the rise, and holidays once again coming and going without my family meeting Ava, my mind turned over again to the IEA report that seemed to live in my brain like a nervous bird in an unwanted cage. I decided to try tapping into the abyss—social media—posting a request for authors to contribute to *Greener Data*—and unexpectedly woke up to dozens of responses.

The following pages are the top 24 authors who contributed their ideas, their innovations, their research and their hearts, offering global perspectives and real-world expertise. Each chapter stands as its own, with its own unique writer's perspective.

Many of these authors have dedicated their careers to building critical data infrastructure, connecting the internet and connecting lives. Many of them have helped businesses, educational networks, hospitals, governments, and more find connection through this pandemic. Many of them have children of their own. All of them believe that together we can.

Several weeks later, February 2022, this world changed yet again with Russia invading Ukraine, and we wrote our chapters with a new sense of urgency. *Greener Data* stands for hope for our children and their children, and it's a testament that even as people in power are choosing to hurt and invade and murder, we are choosing science, faith, enlightenment, connection, love and technology, to turn back the damage and get green.

Our race is against time, and against our own destructive selves. But if we can lead, even in these dark times, our light will shine through and there will be hope for life here on Earth, for our Avas.

As you read the following chapters, highlight the words that inspire you. Consider the collection of ideas and solutions as your baseline for how you can innovate and act in your hometown. You may need to modify these ideas to fit within your climate, your location, your access to resources. But take small steps, quickly, and together we will spark a necessary movement.

So as our children's eyes fill with wonder, and look up to us with questions, let it be said that we gathered answers, listened, innovated, tested, trusted and provided. Our Avas deserve a clean sustainable home and future. Humanity deserves better. It is up to our generation to provide. We are on this watch. And we need to do better.

Jaymie Scotto Cutaia with her daughter, Ava Capri

ONE

Mary Allen & François Sterin

BUILDING TO NET ZERO

Data center operators face a carbon conundrum that begs intensified action on sustainability. While data is growing at an exponential rate, the delivery of data center services to meet this relentless expansion of demand entails a huge increase in energy consumption—carbon impact that we cannot afford at this critical juncture in our efforts to limit global warming. How can operators take advantage of new opportunity associated with digital trans-formation, while at the same time holding the line on carbon? At OVHcloud, we've been grappling with this carbon conundrum throughout our twenty-year history, and have outlined here key approaches that have helped us quickly build capacity, while better managing our overall carbon footprint.

Animated by a spirit of 'frugality' that East European émigré founder Octave Klaba instilled in the OVHcloud organizational culture, we have engaged on multiple fronts to reduce resource waste and improve the bottom line, shrinking carbon impact in the process. We began our sustainability journey with the early adoption of tools and technologies that can drive better environ-mental performance in facilities. Our success in this mission lies in the application of an 'industrial model' that enables OVHcloud to rapidly expand service capacity and to deploy water cooling at scale; OVHcloud now runs a fleet of 400,000 servers on water cooling, one of the largest implementations of its kind anywhere.

But our activities are not limited to our own operations; we continue to innovate solutions up the stack to engage all stake-holders in an ever more ambitious environmental agenda. As a cloud services provider that builds its own servers, OVHcloud must contend with the carbon impact—half of the organization's total—from their manufacture, while working to mitigate the impact of customers who maintain broad independence in their usage of cloud services. On this score, September 2019 presented a defining moment for our team. When we launched a customized server boasting 4 GPUs and 2 CPUs per 1U server for a cloud-based gaming company, the highly dense unit consumed almost 1 kW of power per U and 40 kW per rack. But would this new server encourage additional usage/power consumption that was not useful to society, and did it contribute unduly to the uncon-trolled acceleration of IT impact on the environment? And if we did not provide it, would an alternative vendor deliver this capa-bility with the same carbon profile we could achieve with 4 water blocks? The answer to these questions helped us to define our vision: not only would we continue to refine and build the most efficient and least environmentally impactful data center infrastructure possible, we would also offer customers and suppliers the data they needed to enable the entire ecosystem to work together on articulating operational best practices, on the collective design of the most efficient end-user services.

Today, the OVHcloud sustainability team works towards the fulfillment of a six-point green plan aimed at the achievement of Net Zero emissions by 2030.[1] Given the enormous potential carbon impact associated with the rapid expansion of data center demand and its climate consequences, as a founding member of the EU's Carbon Neutral Data Center Pact, OVHcloud is also reaching out to a broader community, encouraging action on the part of partners, suppliers and clients to better address the looming climate crisis. We will continue to make effective use of conventional data center sustainability inputs; however, we contend that it is no longer just a matter of PUE or the use of renewable energy, rather a full ecosystem view is needed to unify the industry in the fight against climate change.

Water is Cool

Our 'Green Cloud' story opens in 2003, with the design of a water-cooling system that has served as the foundation for reducing energy use across the company's fleet of 33 data centers. As cooling systems typically consume 40 percent of data center power, they have been a first line of attack for environmental improvements in many facilities. For its cooling, OVHcloud chose to develop and implement a technology that was not in broad use at the time, but highly effective in operations.

A year earlier, the company began to assemble its own servers, a space-saving tactic that also enabled the direct deployment of heat exchangers to cool processors and other heat-emitting components. The proprietary system brings liquid inside servers for precision cooling; approximately 70 percent of the heat generated by the servers is captured, then piped through a closed loop system that brings heated liquid to the building exterior for cooling, and cool liquid back to the IT infrastructure. By 2006, OVHcloud was able to run its first server room without air conditioning, and by 2007, to open a new data center at Roubaix without air conditioning, a set up that the company has worked to deploy across its facilities. By eliminating the need for air-cooling infrastructure, including server fans, chillers, air channels and filters, this approach delivers significant energy cost savings. For example, water-to- the chip cooling has eliminated the need for server fans, resulting in a substantial reduction of power to process the same workload, in the range of 20-30 percent, when compared with the operation of more traditional OEM equipment. Across systems, one researcher estimates that liquid cooling uses five times less energy than air cooling, and that precision techniques deliver 1000 times more capacity to extract heat from electronics than do air-cooling solutions.[2]

OVHcloud water cooling vs. fan cooling, heat sink

Simple in design, OVHcloud's closed loop water cooling system has undergone many iterations, with several patented innovations to the water block that sits on the CPU (or GPU) aimed at increasing precision, cooling efficiency and reliability. Significant investment in experimentation with water pressure, flow rate, temperature, pipe diameter, materials, block design—and production at scale—have led to considerable performance enhancements. While the optimal performance of the first generations of water blocks was 60W with a water temperature of 30°C, by 2017, new approaches to addressing the heat requirements of increasingly dense server infrastructure enabled optimal performance of 200W at a water temperature of 30°C.[3] System enhancements have also improved resource efficiency. OVHcloud data centers run at a WUE of 0.2 L/kWh, a water use metric that compares favorably with the industry average of 1.8. Put another way, the company takes a glass of water to cool down a server for ten hours, while the industry average is a full bottle.

OVHcloud water blocks (WB)

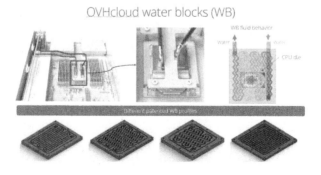

At OVHcloud, water cooling accounts for approximately 70 percent of cooling needs; the remaining 30 percent is delivered at most sites through carbon light, free air-cooling systems.[4] Together, these two cooling technologies have helped the company achieve a respectable PUE score. Across its facilities, OVHcloud reports a PUE ranging from 1.1 to 1.3, results that position the company at the leading edge of hyperscale providers in terms of energy efficiency: only a handful of providers have achieved a PUE of less than 1.2 .[5]

Today's Challenge - Pushing the Limits on Environmental Innovation

A PUE of 1.0 is the Holy Grail in data center efficiency, an operational ideal that becomes more elusive the closer one approaches. In large, hyperscale facilities, operators have made significant strides towards managing energy consumption on the facilities side (PUE is a measure of energy use in facilities, not IT infrastructure). Is it possible to improve on a PUE of 1.2 if 1.0 is a perfect score?

OVHcloud has taken up this challenge with experimentation in yet another technology—immersion cooling (IC). Our new hybrid system is a self-contained tank unit for immersing the server that takes advantage of two cooling fluids. Water is sent to the CPU/GPUs, which evacuates heat outside the data center via a pumping system; and IC fluid is used to cool all of the server's components in addition to the chips. In the IC fluid, hot particles rise and the colder ones sink, providing natural convection that requires no additional mechanical equipment to circulate cool liquid where it is needed. Since processor cooling water is supplied to the servers at a lower temperature than that of the IC fluid, this water is also used in turn to cool the fluid via passive serpentine copper pipes installed in the tank.

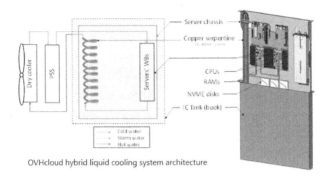

OVHcloud hybrid liquid cooling system architecture

We think of this hybrid system as a library filled with books. In this analogy, the server is a book with its own cover and content, as it is submerged in its own tank and cooled independently. The server rack becomes an IT library, comprised of 48 or 24 IC tanks (books) that contain 48 1U servers, or 24 2U servers. In line with OVHcloud's industrial model, this architecture allows for easy deployment and scale. Since the technology is currently proof of concept, firm metrics on its use in production are not yet available. However, in addition to projections for reduced CAPEX and OPEX gained through simplification of design and infrastructure, the hybrid system holds good promise to lower PUE due to the reduced power consumption for dry coolers/pumps that are no longer needed, to lower WUE due to the elimination of evaporative cooling in dry coolers, and new potential for the reuse of hot water. It also uses biodegradable, non-corrosive fluids (no ozone depleting or global warming potential) and by eliminating rack fans, reduces noise pollution.

Once the 'low hanging fruit' has been picked—deployment of hot aisle, cold aisle air containment, free air cooling, for example —these more technically sophisticated approaches are required. But ongoing efforts to improve PUE values may offer diminishing returns. At a certain point, further optimization of cooling and other systems in the data center can become quite expensive (in terms of financial investment, or even carbon), and innovative technologies that may be beneficial can disrupt existing workloads, while taking time and money to implement at scale. This is the case with brownfield facilities in particular. To extend the lifespan of data centers and the structures that house them, OVHcloud has repurposed existing industrial buildings rather than build new, avoiding the creation of additional embedded carbon. But reuse entails the need to address the impact of legacy infrastructure, which cannot easily be improved in terms of PUE without hefty investments.

Thinking Around the Box Through Circularity in the Data Center

To build on PUE achievements, many data center operators are looking to extend carbon savings into the IT load. Energy efficiency improvements to servers, other systems and IT components are an important means to reducing energy consumption, cost and associated carbon. But the adoption of circular economy principles is another approach that offers additional potential; in a data center context, circularity involves the use of renewable energy, and the elimination of waste through the redesign of products, systems and business models.[6]

OVHcloud's sustainability strategy encompasses key aspects of circular design, including the reuse, upcycle, and recycle of resources for the elimination of carbon and other waste. At a fundamental level, the company's 'industrial' approach to the build and operation of data center sites enables strict control of supply chain inputs to ensure reliability and environmental performance, while standardized deployment of equipment produces economies of scale that can limit waste. OVHcloud is a long-standing recycler of components—the company's goal is to reach zero waste to landfill in production centers—and in upstream procurement, requires a Code of Conduct from suppliers that includes detailed environmental reporting, which is then incorporated into OVHcloud scope 3 carbon accounting. The company is now collaborating with top suppliers to increase the accuracy of their reporting, a critical step since the current range of confidence with scope 3 inputs is 80 percent. This translates to a potential 80 percent error on scope 3 data for IT components, which in turn account for 50 percent of OVHcloud's total impact. Managing sustainability inputs in the supply chain is a vital factor in decarbonization; depending on the industry, a company's value chain can account for up to 95 percent of the carbon emissions related to the business.[7] Accurate and transparent data will enable collective action that amplifies the efforts of individual supply chain members.

While waste management has a clear financial benefit, today it accounts for a small share of the company's carbon accounting (less than 0.1 percent), and so better represents OVHcloud's philosophical determination to derive sustainable outcomes where possible than absolute carbon reduction potential. Far greater results are produced from the lifecycle assessment of servers. In production, server assets currently account for 39 percent of the company's emissions, and so warrant most attention and program focus.[8] OVHcloud's server program offers a classic example of the '3Rs'—it reduces energy consumption, reuses servers and components, and recycles what cannot be refurbished. The company engages in constant monitoring of servers, and any slowdown signals the need for testing, and an evaluation of all components to determine the equipment's potential for repair, repurpose or parts recovery. Today, 100 percent of components are sorted and valued; 34 percent of components that are used are refurbished ones; and the company has created a tiered service offering that provides discounts for clients who chose a reused server (typically, for non-critical workloads). Within IT infrastructure, OVHcloud has created other solutions that are tailor-made for specific use cases, which can optimize energy consumption. For example, cold archive technology that uses magnetic bands has a significantly lower impact than storage on a hard drive. However, server lifecycle assessment offers best potential for carbon reduction, as this equipment runs in volume in the data center and is the primary consumer of power.

Sectoral Impact and the Climate Crisis

Media focus on the large, energy-hungry compute plant has created a negative image of the data center in popular consciousness. Less well recognized is the vision of a sector that is responding in a responsible way to the current climate crisis. The IT industry's potential to mitigate carbon impacts in other sectors has been documented since 2008: according to the most recent GeSI research initiative, emissions avoided through use of ICT are 10 times greater than emissions generated through its deployment, and by 2030, the ICT sector's emissions footprint is expected to decrease to 1.97 percent of the global total.[9] In the data center world, though demand for data has increased rapidly over the past decade, the energy intensity of data centres has declined, due to hardware and facilities innovation and to a shift towards greater reliance the more efficient, cloud-based service provider resources.[10]

Ultimately, however, it's not certain that carbon reduction innovation can keep pace with the increased data demand associated with digital transformation that is now underway in our business and social lives. Growth in Internet data center markets has been estimated at a CAGR of 13.4 percent over the 2020-2027 period, reflecting the accelerated use of internet-related services during Covid-19 pandemic lockdowns.[11] Growth of 5G and IoT deployments are expected to drive additional data usage. At the same time, countries around the world have struggled unsuccessfully with activities to reduce carbon emissions to a level that would limit global warming to the 1.5°C recommended by scientists in the IPCC. Recognizing the significant risk posed by our increasing reliance on technology, and 'business as usual' in many data center operations, the EU has included ICT in the European Green Deal. It has recommended more ambitious GHG emissions reduction targets more broadly, calling on data centers to become climate neutral by 2030.[12]

Engage the Ecosystem

Responding to science-based calls for data center operators to ramp up environmental programming, OVHcloud has committed to achieving Net Zero by 2030. But the company is also stepping beyond the walls of its own organization to engage peers and adjacent organizations in efforts to improve their environmental profiles. At an industry level, OVHcloud is a founding member of the EU's Climate Neutral Datacenter Pact, a self-regulating initiative that pledges cloud/data center operators and trade associations to achieve climate neutrality by 2030 through: energy efficiency improvement, use of carbon-free energy, water conservation, reuse/repair and recycle of servers, and heat recycling. Today, signatories to the pact represent 90 percent of the industry in Europe and most of its key players.[13]

Closer to home, the company is also involving a new constituency in efforts to reduce carbon impact associated with the use of OVHcloud services—the customer. Though OVHcloud operations are increasingly sustainable, the customer that consumes more services will have a more substantial footprint. To help this group achieve more ambitious sustainability goals, OVHcloud is working with Inria, the French National Institute for Research in Digital Science and Technology, to develop a set of metrics that clients can use to measure their progress towards carbon emissions targets. The long-term goal is to offer data related to client's energy consumption, as well as the impact of OVHcloud hardware manufacturing and operations in a package that covers carbon emissions, water consumption, resource depletion, and primary energy consumption for products and services. Currently, OVHcloud provides information from the company's dedicated bare metal server offering on energy consumed by applications, per server each year; energy data can be delivered at the circuit, or even at the Virtual Machine (VM) level. Still in beta, the project has been tested with over ten customers from a range of industries, who are looking to improve the accuracy of their own carbon calculations, to provide precise information on carbon to their own end-users, or to define low-carbon trajectories for a better carbon bill.

Extend Impact

Reaching 2030 Net Zero goals will require a multi-pronged effort on the part of all businesses. OVHcloud's own green plan identifies six action areas: carbon neutrality; developing energy maturity through greater integration of renewables; energy impact monitoring; circular economy strategies; and sustainable procurement in supply chain. Some of these initiatives will prove more timely and some more effective; in carbon accounting, the purchase of renewable energy and extending server lifespans accounts for 80 percent of OVHcloud's total effort. However, the company's mid-term goal is emissions reduction for all three scopes, along with the implementation of a carbon capture program to address its carbon balance, as a step towards carbon neutrality.

For data center operators, a mix of these tactics can be employed to good effect, based on the business' unique market circumstance and production environment. But success will depend on the articulation of a comprehensive and strategic plan that identifies achievable milestones and associated metrics. For companies looking to leverage IT as a means of achieving their own environmental goals, due diligence into cloud provider capabilities should focus on the type of energy that is used, server lifespans, cooling systems, and transparency of the provider's reporting data, with an eye to choosing the cloud provider with the lowest impact in terms of carbon, water and hardware lifecycles. Potential clients should also weigh the data use case: data sobriety—or the consumption of data services only when necessary—will be key in the fight against climate change.

OVHcloud has outlined a complex set of interrelated actions and redoubled its efforts to create and implement sustainable technologies in facilities, in IT infrastructure and beyond. By extending the possibility of greater decarbonization through work with a growing ecosystem, the company is hoping to encourage the broad social/community action that can demonstrate the data center industry's progress on climate. This approach is especially critical today, a time when industry forecasts predict inexorable growth in data usage, to ensure IT realizes its potential as an enabler, rather than as an enemy of planetary health. If this entails higher prices/reduced volumes for cloud providers, OVHcloud has accepted this responsibility, and will leverage its leadership in the deployment an efficient platform with low environmental impact in customer and supplier education to encourage others to also do the right thing.

---

1. Allen, M. 2020, July. "OVHcloud: Sustainable by Design. A DC Foresight Report." InsightaaS. July 2020.
2. Craig, D. 2020. "Liquid cooling at the Edge – the coming technology is already here." Techerati. April 2020. https://techerati.com/features-hub/opinions/liquid-cooling-at-the-edge-the-coming-technology-is-already-here/.
3. Chehade, Ali. 2019. "Water cooling: from innovation to disruption – Parts I and II." OVHCloud. December 2019. https://blog.ovhcloud.com/water-cooling-from-innovation-to-disruption-part-i/
   https://blog.ovhcloud.com/water-cooling-from-innovation-to-disruption-part-ii/.
4. OVHcloud has expanded its data center fleet through greenfield build, use of colocation services and acquisition. In some facilities, such as the Virginia data center acquired from VMware, the company inherited traditional chiller systems, while in some regions, such as Poland, the data centers run on electricity generated by a coal powered grid. To reach Net Zero goals, the company will offset this impact through other measures, such as the purchase of renewable energy credits.
5. The global PUE estimate reported by the Uptime Institute for data centers of all sizes in 2020 was 1.58, and the European data center PUE average was 1.46.
   Andy Lawrence. 2020. "Data Center PUEs have been flat since 2013." DCD. 2020. https://www.datacenterdynamics.com/en/opinions/data-center-pues-have-been-flat-2013/.
   Andy Lawrence. 2020. "Which regions have the most energy efficient data centers?" Uptime Institute. 2020. https://journal.uptimeinstitute.com/datacenter-energy-efficiency-by-region/
6. World Economic Forum, Ellen MacArthur Foundation and McKinsey & Co. 2015. "From linear to circular—Accelerating a proven concept." World Economic Forum. https://reports.weforum.org/toward-the-circular-economy-accelerating-the-scale-up-across-global-supply-chains/from-linear-to-circular-accelerating-a-proven-concept/.
7. World Economic Forum. 2021. "Net-Zero Challenge: The supply chain opportunity." Insight Report. file:///C:/Users/MARYL/AppData/Local/Temp/WEF_Net_Zero_Challenge_The_Supply_Chain_Opportunity_2021.pdf.

8. OVHcloud. 2020. "Carbon Balance: Our results for FY20." OVHCloud. file:///C:/Users/MARYL/AppData/Local/Temp/Carbon% 20Balance_OVHcloud_FY20.pdf

9. GeSI and Accenture. 2015. "#SMARTer2030. ICT Solutions for 21st Century Challenges." Global e-Sustainability Initiative and Accenture Strategy. 2015. https://www.gesi.org/research/smarter2030-ict-solutions-for-21st-century-challenges.

10. Researchers calculated an increase in global data demand that was more than six-fold for 2010-2018, while data center energy consumption rose by only 6%..
    Eric Masanet, Arman Shehabi, Nuoa Lei, Sarah Smith, and Jonathan Koomey. 2020. "Recalibrating global data center energy-use estimates." *Science* 367, no. 6481 (2020) in "How Much Energy Do Data Centers Really Use?" Energy Innovation, Policy & Technology. March 2020. https:// energyinnovation.org/2020/03/17/how-much-energy-do-data-centers-really-use/.

11. Research and Markets. 2021. "Internet Data Centers - Global Market Trajectory & Analytics." Research and Markets. April 2021. https://www. researchandmarkets.com/reports/2228038/ internet_data_centers_global_market_trajectory?utm_source=CI& utm_medium=PressRelease&utm_code=dr69qt&utm_campaign=1584987+-+ Global+Internet+Data+Centers+Market+Report+2021%3a+U.S.+Market+ is+Estimated+at+%2416+Billion%2c+While+China+is+Forecast+to+Grow+ at+17.5%25+CAGR+by+2027&utm_exec=chdo54prd

12. EU Commission. 2020. "Green cloud and green data centres. Shaping Europe's Digital Future." European Commission. https://digital-strategy.ec. europa.eu/en/policies/green-cloud.

13. Climate Neutral Data Centre Pact. n.d. https://www. climateneutraldatacentre.net/.

About the Author

MARY ALLEN

An IT trend watcher with a keen eye on sustainability, Mary has travelled the globe in journalist, analyst, and consultant roles. As editorial director, she has created and executed on content strategy for several IT-focused websites; as group facilitator, she has worked with technical and business experts to co-create leading edge best practice guidance; and as innovator, she has co-founded two businesses that uniquely combine media and IT market research delivery. Mary is a writer and thinker with deep understanding of technologies at the leading edge, and an appreciation for the challenges organizations may encounter in their implementation.

Mary has authored hundreds of articles, reports, whitepapers, and books on the full spectrum of IT subjects. But she is most inspired sharing information on sustainability, which she has continued to do even when green IT was considered the adversary of data centre uptime—from founding of the GreenerIT website, through a stint as sustainable IT columnist for Bloomberg BNA, and more recently in communities of practice developed through InsightaaS community work. In this chapter, she continues a collaboration with OVHcloud aimed at the identifying key technologies and processes that enable data centre operators to achieve the twin 'ecos' – economic and environmental benefits.

About the Author

FRANÇOIS STERIN

François has held executive roles in all areas of infrastructure for IT and cloud, including data center and energy, server manufacturing and supply chain, network infrastructure, and content distribution, across all continents. Through his career, he has built unique understanding of hyperscaler challenges, translating a decade's worth of experience as head of the data center and energy portfolio at Google to OVHcloud, the rapid growth European leader in cloud services delivery. At OVHcloud, François serves as a key contributor to organizational growth; he has articulated an operational strategy and manages engineering activities to ensure reliability and scalability of the company's service delivery infrastructure, based on a concept of 'industrialization' that has supported rapid scale of the OVHcloud fleet.

François' broad and deep infrastructure expertise has enabled him to speak authoritatively on sustainable design in the data center, and to elevate sustainability in OVHcloud's recent rebranding as a core corporate operating principle. The company's commitment to greener data is evident in the OVHcloud sustainability plan, developed by François' team to guide green activities in a manner designed to achieve defined, science-based target outcomes.

TWO

Garry Connolly

BIODIVERSITY–MORE THAN JUST A BUZZ WORD

We are in the midst of the Fourth Industrial Revolution, where we are seeing a blurring of the boundaries between the physical, digital, and biological worlds. Data today is what steam was to the first Industrial Revolution of 1760-1840. Data, along with the centers where the data lives, has become an integral part of our daily lives. Unfortunately, the data centers themselves have been rather misunderstood. The buildings are sometimes thought of as secretive and austere gray "boxes" that are disconnected from their local communities. There is a misperception that they add little to the communities they reside in despite the economic benefits they provide.

One of the biggest complaints about the industry is sustainability. Against the backdrop of Net Zero policies and the drive to reduce carbon emissions, data centers appear to be at odds with greater sustainability goals and objectives. One area that could play a key role, and is often overlooked, is the role of data center campuses and buildings and how they are integrated into the local community.

As Data Centre Magazine states: "There's plenty of discussion about what the data center of the future will look like. Usually, these discussions revolve around liquid cooling, intelligent power management, and even quantum high-performance computing hardware. But given the size of footprint that data centers occupy across the world, discussions should also be taking place about how these external spaces cannot just minimize their impact on the environment, but actively benefit local biodiversity."[1]

Championing biodiversity is one area of common purpose where the data center industry can collaborate with their local communities. I have seen first-hand how, with careful planning and mindfulness of unintended consequences, there is a real opportunity for data centers to positively impact the local biodiversity of the communities they reside in.

Why is Biodiversity so Important?

Biodiversity is the variety of life in a particular habitat or ecosystem, and currently, biodiversity loss is happening at an unparalleled rate, with bees particularly endangered. Pollinators are vital to the growth of pollinator-dependent food crops to the tune of $577 billion worldwide.[2] It's not just crops that are at risk. We know that three quarters of our wildflowers benefit from being pollinated by insects – without bees, we lose the colorful and distinct natural beauty of our landscape.[3]

A typical honeybee can visit 50-1000 flowers in one trip.[4] If each bee takes ten trips a day, a colony with 25,000 forager bees can pollinate 250 million flowers in a day.[5] To protect pollination service, we need healthy honeybees, but we also need to have an abundance and diversity of wild bees, as well as other insects like flies, moths, and butterflies.

Rare species are disappearing through habitat loss and our common species are struggling because the way we currently manage the rest of the landscape means there simply isn't enough food for them to survive. Once a species is extinct, it cannot be reversed. The balance of nature is affected forever.

Dr. Úna FitzPatrick, co-founder and project manager of the All-Ireland Pollinator Plan, provided some important context for me on this issue last year. "Unfortunately, we are the generation who have guarded over the disappearance of our biodiversity. We have created a new normal where nature is rare, rather than something we live with and are part of. Bringing back wild pollinators means returning more native flowers to our landscape. More flowers means more fruits and seeds and therefore more birds and mammals. More flowers also means a more distinct, more colorful and more attractive environment for us to live and work in."

How a Community Makes a Difference

When we founded Host in Ireland in 2014, the objective was to get competitors to park their ego—and their balance sheet—at the door and work together. We continue to engage from a place of collaboration by doing the right thing, for the right reasons, at the right time with the right people.

These principles have served us well as an organization, but they are also the foundation needed to tackle larger societal change. You can only address challenges like biodiversity or the climate crisis with a strong community already established. As our broader communities continue to recover from the effects of the Covid pandemic, creating a sense of collective purpose has become an even more critical part of this recovery.

We did just that in 2019 with the launch of our DCs for Bees initiative. Through this program, we are providing a means for organization and community purpose-based activity which fosters an appreciation for protecting and encouraging biodiverse habitats in our local areas. By coming together as an industry, we are leveraging the work of experts and resources in order to have the greatest impact and maximize the ripple effect of our actions.

Saving Irish Bees One Step at a Time

In Ireland, bees contribute to 70% of our crops, but sadly, 33% of Irish bees are facing extinction, including almost 90% of our bumblebees by 2050 at the current rate of decline.[6] With the DCs for Bees initiative, we have pledged to raise awareness, advocate, and most importantly, take—and inspire others to take—action to make Ireland more pollinator-friendly and ensure the survival of our pollinators for future generations.

Like any ecosystem, biodiversity is very delicate, and throughout the world we are seeing the unintended consequences of non-native trees, bushes, and crops being planted in the wrong habitats. Any plan implemented needs to be developed in cooperation with local biodiversity owners. From the start, we have worked alongside the Irish National Biodiversity Centre and the All-Ireland Pollinator Plan. These organizations are leading the way in reversing the trend of population reduction of bees in Ireland through research-based, ethical, and indigenous methods. This collaboration has ensured the actions we take mitigate the resulting consequences and are as impactful as possible.

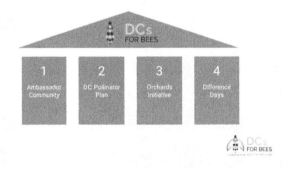

The first pillar of the DCs for Bees program was the creation of Difference Days to provide an opportunity for individuals to contribute to their local community. Over 100 volunteers from companies who design, build, supply, service, and operate the data center community in Ireland came together to plant more than 2000 indigenous Irish trees in County Wicklow in a single day. This particular project was to help halt the worrying decline of a species of the wall butterfly which is endangered in Ireland.

The DCs for Bees Ambassadors are individuals from the Irish

data center community that have come together out of personal desire to create a movement dedicated to halting the decline of bees in Ireland. Ambassadors have a genuine interest in biodiversity, the environment, and bees and are enthused to make a real difference. Collaborating in monthly meetings, the 35 ambassadors discuss ideas, actions taken and results achieved so that as a community we can become more effective advocates. Overall our ambassadors have access to influence over a million employees worldwide within their organizations, not counting their communities and outside networks.

From learning about the placement of bee hotels to the blend of indigenous species for a data center campus, the DCs for Bees Pollinator Plan is the world's first data center industry plan created specifically to drive awareness and action to help reduce, stall or even reverse the extinction of our bees. Any business in the data center ecosystem—from the smallest supplier to the largest data landowners—can implement one or more of the 42 actionable items outlined in the plan.

"The specific plan of action in the DCs for Bees Pollinator Plan makes it easy to roll out across our company and gives our employees a tangible way to give back to our community," said Matt Pullen, EVP and Managing Director, Europe at CyrusOne. "As with our broader involvement in Host in Ireland, being a part of a collective provides an opportunity to have a bigger, longer lasting impact. For something as important as Ireland's biodiversity, we are very proud to be a part of this program."

Orchards have played an important role in communities for many centuries, providing a focal point, a gathering space, and a place where people and nature successfully work together to create abundant harvests. As the final pillar of the program, Orchards in the Community was launched in 2021 to plant nearly 1300 orchards in every county throughout the entire island of Ireland. The orchards will provide vital green spaces in our cities and towns, where people are encouraged to interact with nature either through becoming custodians of the trees or by simply being around them and enjoying their shade, beauty and fruit. They are also important habitats as the natural life cycle of fruit trees provides food sources for pollinators and other species throughout the year.

Making a Holistic Difference

The DCs for Bees initiative has enabled the Irish data center community to become a greater part of its local communities. This is important because the social contract of any community requires an implicit agreement among the members of a society to cooperate for the greater good. Data centers may take resources from a community, but they also need to give back and offer an olive branch into the community as well.

The Orchards project has seen organizations donate orchards for a wide variety of purposes. Some have been planted to rejuvenate existing orchards. Others are rewilding land to repair damaged ecosystems and restore landscapes. Schools are receiving orchards to become part of the life science curriculum focusing on fruit and insects. Charities are also reaping the benefits with orchard donations.

Global law firm, Eversheds Sutherland, donated 40 orchards for the grounds of the children's charity, Barretstown, for children and their families living with a serious illness to enjoy as part of their camp activities. "Our goal at Barretstown is to provide our families with a chance to unwind, destress and enjoy quality family-time together in a fun, safe and relaxing environment," said Tim O'Dea, Director of Development at Barretstown. "The orchards will provide a wealth of activities for our campers to enjoy as they connect with nature and learn more about the life cycle of pollinators and their environments."

In addition to making the communities better places to live, work and play, the data centers themselves are rethinking how they integrate their land into the community. Data center operators are looking at how they use roof space for gardens and wall space for living walls/vertical gardens. Data center operators are opening acres of lands for biodiversity and local community use and enjoyment.

Cyrus One, for example, has made a commitment to habitat a part of their global sustainability plans. New facilities are incorporating biodiverse habitats into their building plans and older facilities are being retrofitted where possible. Keppel Data Centres have enhanced their facilities' landscapes in Ireland to be more pollinator friendly by planting hawthorn shrubs around the perimeter and sowing more than 800 bluebell bulbs as both of these plants are good pollen sources for bees. The same goes for Equinix who are planting orchards, pollinator friendly plants, and bee hotels as part of incorporating pollinator-friendly designs into their campuses.

What Comes Next?

As part of the larger climate crisis, the plight of the pollinators has a very real impact on our local communities. As more work gets underway to address these issues, the time has come to think outside the box about the role "data" and "centers" can play in addressing this issue. This is an opportunity for action—for data center operators globally to become the necessary leaders in how we utilize our land and resources to help pollinators thrive.

As we have demonstrated in Ireland, there is enthusiasm for these kinds of projects. Perhaps more importantly, there is a real commitment to go beyond awareness and advocacy to take the actions needed to make a difference. We've had colleagues around the world express interest in implementing similar projects in their own countries. Our team is working with them on the parameters of the program while they liaise with local organizations to create fit for purpose elements best suited for their local biodiversity. DCs for Bees has become an exemplar of what is possible.

As my 12-year-old is fond of reminding me, unless we stop talking and begin to take real action, bees will no longer be a part of our science class, but a part of history class instead. It's now up to all of us to step up and make a real difference. We have the power to do something for pollinators, biodiversity and the broader climate crisis as a whole, so let's do it.

---

1. Menear, Harry. 2021. "Host in Ireland launches DCs for Bees Pollinator Plan." Data Centre Magazine. April 22, 2021 https://datacentremagazine.com/critical-environments/host-ireland-launches-dcs-bees-pollinator-plan.
2. United Nations. 2016. "Countries urged to prioritize protection of pollinators to ensure food security at UN Biodiversity Conference." United Nations. Dec 6, 2016. https://www.un.org/sustainabledevelopment/blog/2016/12/pollinators/.
3. Host in Ireland. 2021. "DCs for Bees Pollinator Plan." https://www.hostinireland.com/pollinator-plan
4. Morelle, Rebecca. 2016. "Key report makes new tally for number of world's plants." BBC News. May 10, 2016. https://www.bbc.com/news/science-environment-36230858.
5. Bradbear, Nicola. 2008. "Bees and their role in forest livelihoods." Food and Agriculture Organization of the United Nations. Nov 8, 2008. https://www.fao.org/3/i0842e/i0842e00.pdf.
6. Host in Ireland. 2019. "DCs for Bees" https://www.hostinireland.com/dc-s-for-bees.

About the Author

GARRY CONNOLLY

Garry Connolly is the Founder of Host in Ireland, a strategic global initiative created to increase awareness of the benefits of hosting digital assets in Ireland and Irish companies delivering international data centre projects. A self-proclaimed "stubborn digital optimist," Garry is a much sought-after keynote speaker, panelist and moderator at global industry events. He regularly appears in conferences throughout the Globe.

Garry has over 30 years' experience in assisting Foreign Direct investment into Europe. He demonstrates a pragmatic and common sense approach to data centre site selection, sales, negotiation, company start-ups, mentoring and strategic thinking. Based on a philosophy of

doing the right thing with the right people at the right time, Garry was instrumental in developing the GDPR Awareness Coalition and DCs for Bees, a Host in Ireland sub-initiative.

Recognised for his leadership efforts, Garry has been named in the Broadgroup Power 200: The World's Most Influential Data Economy Leaders of 2019, recognised as one of the top 50 EMEA Influencers in Cloud and Data Centres 2017 by Data Economy and was runner up in the 2017 DCS Awards' 'Data Centre Individual of Year' category.

THREE

Erick Contag and Nicole Starosielski, PhD

A CALL FOR CONNECTIVE THINKING

Erick's Journey to Digital Infrastructure

Erick Contag's father was the inspiration that led him to explore high tech and entrepreneurship and to care for nature and the environment. His father started his career at the NASA satellite tracking station outside of Quito, Ecuador. His father's career eventually led him to work on building guidance computers, control systems, analog telecom networks, and later power systems for what was then referred to as computer centers (the granddaddies to our current data centers).

As a result, Erick was immersed in communications, computers, and technology from childhood. During Erick's teenage years, summer internships at his father's company involved installing uninterruptible power supply systems, backup generators, substations, supervisory control systems, among many other systems.

Not knowing what he wanted to study—and torn between architecture and computer science—Erick ended up bringing together both with an electrical engineering degree in computer architecture. He was hooked on the digital world!

Erick landed his first job in San Diego, California. This

opened the opportunity to participate in the design, construction, and operation of the San Diego SuperComputer Center (SDSC), one of the five United States national facilities that focused on tackling Grand Challenge problems.[1] SDSC also became one of the core nodes of the NSFnet—the foundation of today's internet. He was fortunate to work with emerging data networks, high-performance 3D computer graphics systems, and the world's most powerful computers.

Over the years, Erick's curiosity in high-tech and the opportunity to take such technologies to the developing world took him back to South America where he had grown up. There he launched several companies and witnessed hands-on the benefits these technologies had on enterprises and people. He always believed in giving back, and forged alliances with universities helping them to incorporate these technologies and their uses into their curricula, helping to develop the next generation of professionals.

At the height of the internet bubble, Erick returned to the US. Through a close friend, he was introduced to the fiber optic subsea communications world. And once again, he was hooked, and subsequently dove into an amazing career building and operating digital infrastructures.

Looking for a way to give back to the industry that he had come to love, Erick became very involved with the SubOptic Association, eventually stepping up to lead the organization and to create an entirely new entity that would be dedicated to its future: the SubOptic Foundation.

Nicole's Journey to SubSea Systems

Nicole Starosielski, like Erick and many others, had initially believed that the world was connected via satellites. But once she realized that the global communications fabric was built upon subsea cable systems, which have lower latency, higher data carrying capacity, and are very resilient and upgradable, she too became hooked on the industry. She completed a Ph.D. on the subsea cable industry and wrote an entire book, *The Undersea Network*, that focused on the subsea systems that carry more than 99% of all digital communications and connect the continents. Her book and research focused on the social and environmental aspects of these systems: how they emerged in particular places, whether in the global hubs of London or New York, or in places that seem out-of-the-way, but are actually quite central, like Fortaleza, Brazil.

As she met and talked to industry veterans, Nicole realized that subsea networks were unique: they have a marine component unlike many other parts of the digital infrastructure, a wide range of stakeholders, and face challenges escaped by terrestrial networks. They take an enormous amount of international coordination between companies around the world to install and maintain. But as a result, they also bring together people from different backgrounds and cultures. It wasn't just that the networks connected people, but the networkers were also building deep social connections that held the industry together.

Eager to make a difference in the industry and—as a university professor—to construct an educational platform for the future, Nicole started attending the SubOptic conferences. SubOptic, as the premiere organization for the subsea cable industry, is the place where people from different backgrounds, but with a passion for subsea cables, technology, and the environment, could come together as a community.

It was here that Erick and Nicole met, and came up with a plan: one where they could leverage digital infrastructure for change and simultaneously give back to the subsea world.

Connectivity is The Future!

As populations grow and we add the next billion users to the internet, and as devices and smart applications proliferate, we can expect exponential growth of data and the need to build and enhance our global digital infrastructure to support this future demand. There will be more links between people and more growth in the platforms that support them. As 5G is deployed, and as we bring services closer to our customers, these connections will require new infrastructure and more and more capacity. And as machines are interconnected via the Internet of Things (IoT), as we embrace autonomous vehicles, the metaverse, and the next generation of digital services, the quantity of transmissions will multiply exponentially.

Digital infrastructure is and will rapidly expand to meet these needs. Subsea cable systems, terrestrial networks, data centers, and satellites are all integral to global communications. Even though these remain hidden in plain sight, it is atop these critical infrastructure ecosystems that our digital world has been built, and which enables us to seamlessly communicate in high resolution video across the globe, collaborate across a nation's borders, or play online games with someone next door or on the other side of the planet.

New scale and hyperscale data centers are being built to satisfy the need for compute, cloud services and storage, along with distributed network edge colocation facilities. New subsea systems offer more and more international capacity. Devices proliferate in both consumer and commercial domains. All of this digital infrastructure runs on energy.

Just as the future will see an exponential growth in connectivity, it will also see significant demands in electricity use. The world needs to embrace plans to decarbonize the electric grid, significantly improve power storage, remove the use of gas and oil for heating and cooling, and transition to clean power.[2] Without these changes, a growth in connectivity will continue to contribute to greenhouse emissions and ultimately climate change. In other words, a connected future without sustainability is an ecological disaster. Sustainability is therefore not simply a matter of doing the right thing, it is a matter of security for people, infrastructure and the planet itself.

So we wondered: how should we be thinking about sustainability as we build digital infrastructure for the next generation? We propose that we need not simply focus on building connections for others, but on *connective thinking* ourselves: bridging digital infrastructure to other industrial sectors, economies, and knowledge domains.

As a non-profit dedicated to education and peer-reviewed research, we realized that the SubOptic Foundation could bring awareness to these issues and build insights from the collective intelligence of the subsea cable industry.

Connective Thinking for Sustainability

How do we put connective thinking into action? First of all, as we plan new services for the edge, roll out 5G and other high bandwidth technologies, embrace web 3.0, and connect the many people who still remain offline, we need to rethink the electrical grid and our current energy system. An aging grid and limited battery capacity are constraints for renewable development and thus constraints on digital development. We need a smarter, more flexible, and more capacious energy infrastructure to match the developments in digital infrastructure. Some of this work is already occurring on-site, as digital infrastructure projects construct new wind and solar resources. We need to go further and integrate energy systems thinking into our plans for new development, alongside retrofits.

Such synergies across domains are crucial for building a more sustainable network. We must move beyond simply getting a lot of "mileage" out of our infrastructure. We should be analyzing the new functions our infrastructure might take up and consider the many ways for us to leverage developments in one domain to benefit another. As one example, take the Ford F-150 Lightning— an electric vehicle that is not simply a transportation device or a computer on wheels; it is also a potential backup generator for when one's home power goes out. Instead of purchasing a fossil-fuel powered generator, leveraging the use of one's electric car to power the home reduces potential carbon emissions. It also makes the purchase of electric vehicles more cost-effective in the long run. We need this creative re-thinking of function and purpose in the domain of digital infrastructure.

We also need to ask critical questions that might not have easy answers. For example, once we electrify our transportation systems, we must ask: where does this energy come from? Much electricity generation still relies on fossil fuels or carbon-burning plants. Even if one buys an electric car or builds an efficient data center, understanding the sources of power is crucial to any path to sustainability. *We have to think beyond the plug.*

This kind of connective thinking is already occurring at scale in some digital infrastructure developments. For example, district heating networks leverage the waste heat of data centers to warm nearby homes. Excess data center heat has even been used to heat greenhouses. One recent study showed that using data centers to heat greenhouses in sub-Arctic zones could increase food-sufficiency in the area.[3] Through such partnerships, developments in one sector—like the information economy—can be connected to developments in another, such as agriculture. Furthermore, many larger scale operators have committed to New Zero CO_2 emissions in fairly short order, relying mainly on hydro-electric, solar, and wind power, for their hyperscale facilities. Our hat goes off to those that have committed to a greener future, are thinking out of the box, and acting on it.

How do we build new infrastructure that is more sustainable? This requires connective thinking across the value chain. Within each sector, we need to look at the whole value chain to find places to achieve sustainability. For example, in the subsea network, we need to look not just at operations but also at manufacturing, installation, repair, and recycling. This involves considering everything from plow depth in the seabed, to the amount of armoring on a cable, to the use of new sources of energy across the supply chain, while still maintaining operational resiliency, service quality, and overall network security. How do we increase fuel efficiency or usage of on-shore power supply? New materials and innovation in technology, design, and more efficient operations and maintenance processes are integral parts of the path forward.

Lastly, this kind of connective thinking has to take in the vision of digital infrastructure as a whole, looking at the relative sustainability of component parts. For example, take the subsea cables that carry 99% of transoceanic internet traffic. These cables are environmentally-friendly. They have little effect on the seafloor. They consume relatively little energy. More of these networks can be laid to infrastructure in locations where sustainable interventions have already taken place. Subsea cables and strategically located data centers can be used to unlock the renewable energy resources of places such as the Nordic countries or Northern Canada, and some companies are already looking to do so.

In order to build a better future, we also need to look at both sides of the climate equation: on one side, we need to think about how to unlock natural resources, find ways to move beyond the limitations of batteries or storage, and develop new fuel sources. We currently emit approximately 50 gigatonnes of CO_2 each year. One tonne of CO_2 is the approximate amount released on a round trip flight from London to New York. In the US there are 276 million cars, releasing 1.27 gigatonnes a year. About half of the 50 gigatonnes can be mitigated through decarbonizing the electric grid and other technical advancements. On the other hand, we need to supplement this with removal and sequestration of carbon dioxide through stopping deforestation, protecting nature, and using nature-based solutions. Systematic thinking and collective advancements at speed and scale may get us to Net Zero by 2050; every step and every action counts towards a sustainable future, and it needs to happen now.

The SubOptic Foundation: Building A Sustainable Future for Digital Infrastructure

The SubOptic Foundation, a charitable organization of the subsea cable industry, is deeply invested in building a more sustainable future. Our projects include education and training programs for the benefit of individuals in the industry and the broader community. The Foundation also encourages and actively addresses awareness, inclusivity, and diversity across that population. At the heart of many of these programs is sustainability: social sustainability, the sustainability of the workforce, alongside —and connected to—environmental sustainability.

Powered by industry members' selfless giving of time, energy and ideas, the SubOptic Foundation takes on industry-wide issues that exceed the scope of individual companies and immediate needs, and extends to careful thinking about the long-term future. We ask questions such as: How can we attract the next generation of digital infrastructure professionals? Where will this next generation of subsea cable workers be trained? How will we ensure critical knowledge doesn't get lost in the transition? Can we ensure that the next generation is trained globally and equitably? How will we use our capacity to connect to minimize environmental harm? How can we mitigate our own inevitable environmental footprint? What countries can use cables to unlock their renewable resources?

In 2021 the SubOptic Foundation received a $200,000 grant to launch the Sustainable Subsea Networks research project to begin to answer some of these questions. Foundation research has included developing a carbon footprint of a subsea cable network, cataloging the range of best practices across the industry, and exploring the possibilities for renewable energy at the cable landing station. The Foundation also launched a new publication, the "Sustainable Subsea" column, where stories about positive environmental developments are chronicled as inspiration for the industry. Making data greener requires action across all scales: from the smallest interventions, such as workplace protocols, to the construction of new cable-laying vessels. Sharing stories about how to make our digital infrastructure greener is an essential part of the journey to a more sustainable future.

For example, in one recent story, we observe how the unique nature of the subsea industry demands that we innovate, create, and implement unique solutions. When cable landing stations were first constructed, the concept of efficiently managing airflows for IT equipment was absent, largely because they were

designed for telecom equipment, typically -48VDC optical transmission equipment, and certainly not for current densely-popu-
lated server clusters. However, with the advancement of optical
technology, and significantly higher fiber pair count subsea
systems, and the need—in some cases—for interconnection, engineers are rethinking cable landing stations (CLS); moving away
from large-scale infrastructures to modular designs, allowing to
adapt space, power, and cooling to incoming technologies while
being more efficient and greener. This is an example of how innovative thinking is essential to adaptation.

We believe environmental sustainability can only be achieved
with social sustainability. Therefore, the SubOptic Foundation is
committed to attracting a young and diverse population to the
industry, training and educating them, and giving them the tools
to innovate to solve the problems of the future. This next generation can help us to 'think outside of the box', to design new materials, to unlock the renewable potential of regions such as Norway
and Northern Canada. The Foundation has already started a
global series of yearly local language symposia aimed at college
students and incoming professionals, starting with locations
including Japan and France, which will cultivate the industry's
leaders of tomorrow. The plan is to further develop these
symposia for each major region of our planet.

Lastly, as oceans rise due to climate change and due to the
melting of glaciers and the poles, it will not simply threaten
coastal communities, but their infrastructures, including potentially many cable landing stations around the globe. The
SubOptic Foundation is interested in how global warming will
affect the resiliency of digital infrastructure. Our very capacity to
connect is at stake in this investigation.

Working as a foundation, our charter is to be transparent,
inclusive, and open. Our projects produce knowledge that will
benefit the subsea and digital infrastructure industries. This kind
of investment, however, goes beyond the scope of any one
company. In order to address climate change, there must be significantly more investment from governments, public funding agen-

cies, and philanthropists, alongside venture capitalists and private sector finance. The Foundation's work supports the subsea sector as a whole and takes a broad view to create synergies across the industry. Our research is open access and our educational programs are available to all. We invite you to participate and join us in the development of the next generation of digital infrastructure professionals and building a more sustainable future.

A Call to Action

We close this chapter with a call to action. We call for the industry support and development of forward-looking programs with sustainability at their core. We need to do this at scale. If we think about these problems linearly, we will be left behind. We don't have time to take the traditional sequential approach. We need to move at speed. We need to think big. We need open education and research. We need broader and more connective thinking that can bring us to the new solutions we need to address climate change. We need to commit to our communities, find ways to give back, reconnect with nature, and build a greener future together.

---

1. Grand Challenge problems can expand the frontiers of human knowledge about ourselves and the world around us. These may be related to energy, health, education, the environment, national security, and global development. They can also serve as a "North Star" for collaboration between the public and private sectors. https://www.nsf.gov/news/special_reports/big_ideas/convergent.jsp

2. Doerr, John. 2021. *Speed & Scale: An Action Plan for Solving Our Climate Crisis Now.* Penguin Random House.

3. H.M. Ljungqvist, M Risberg L Mattsson, and M. Vesterlund. 2021. "Data center heated greenhouses, a matter for enhanced food self-sufficiency in sub-arctic regions," Energy 215, p. 119-169.

About the Author

ERICK CONTAG

Erick Contag is strategist who is passionate about building and operating sustainable digital infrastructures. He has over 30 years of executive management, entrepreneurship, marketing & sales, and business development expertise. Mr. Contag has been responsible for managing C-level relationships and telecommunications/high-technology projects for start-up enterprises through large multi-national and Global 100 companies. He has proven success in starting, building, and operating telecommunications/subsea networks, and colocation/data centers infrastructure and high-tech businesses. In 2011 & 2013, he was awarded the Global Telecoms Business Power 100 Award, an honor bestowed upon the most powerful 100 executives in the telecom industry.

Mr. Contag has held executive positions in the U.S. and Latin America and serves on the Board of Directors of several companies and associations. He believes in giving back to society through education and research programs. Mr. Contag holds a degree in Electrical Engineering from the University of Tulsa, an Executive Engineering Management certification from Instituto de Estudios Superiores de Administración (IESA), and recently attended the Executive Program at Singularity University.

About the Author

NICOLE STAROSIELSKI, PHD

Nicole Starosielski, Associate Professor of Media, Culture, and Communication at New York University, is author and co-editor of many books on media, infrastructure, and environments: The Undersea Network (2015), Media Hot and Cold (2021), Signal Traffic: Critical Studies of Media Infrastructure (2015), Sustainable Media: Critical Approaches to Media and Environment (2016), and Assembly Codes: The Logistics of Media (2021). Her research focuses on the history of the cable industry, the social aspects of submarine cable construction and maintenance, and the paths toward industry sustainability. She is the co-convener of SubOptic's Global Citizen Working Group and Lead Researcher on the SubOptic Foundation's Sustainable Subsea Networks Project.

FOUR

Sean Farney, Brad Meissner, & Melissa Reali-Elliott

POWERING A BETTER FUTURE: KOHLER'S EVOLUTIONARY AND REVOLUTIONARY APPROACHES

The Data-Centered World

The world today is more complex than ever, and we've experienced an explosion of digital infrastructure capacity and reliability. Almost overnight, data center facilities morphed from a pedestrian warehouse full of computers enabling "nice to haves" like social media, online shopping, and video streaming into "must haves," always-on, income-generating lynchpins of daily business productivity.

Considering the rapidity of change and growing interconnectedness of the global economy, it's no exaggeration to say that we've reached the point in the Fourth Industrial Revolution where data has become the currency of both social culture and business value creation. Therefore, data centers are now foundational in the production of global industrial capital, a "data-centered economy," so to speak. With bits and bytes as currency, access must be universal and guaranteed.

Corporate agendas as well as public policy changes will drive many sustainability gains over the next decade. While these targets may fluctuate, the ultimate goal remains the same: reduce global data center carbon footprint. The good news is that the data center industry has preempted this evolving requirement with the introduction of new sustainable innovations. Data center companies and providers, such as Kohler, are leading the way with initiatives that reduce environmental impact dramatically.

Kohler takes a universal approach to its social efforts, such as sustainability impact, and considers how its initiatives work to address long-term well-being and prosperity for the planet. Our passion for preserving the planet fosters fresh ideas and new ways of doing business. Over a century of design and engineering expertise as a power provider grants us the opportunity to lead all of our businesses to meet the obligation to implement and promote more sustainable choices, enabling not just energy reductions, but also a smarter, more efficient way of working.

We all know data's rising eminence has a dark side. Data center growth drives more highly-engineered facility redundancy and fault tolerance, starting with power systems. Inherently, they are energy intensive, consuming up to 50 times as much electricity per square foot as the average commercial building[1]—and when this electricity comes from fossil fuels, it contributes to global warming.

This means more generators, more testing, more diesel fuel burn, and more pollutant emissions. This consequence is in direct conflict with another rising force now at the forefront of the data center industry: sustainability. We need greener growth in our industry. How can we balance our decadent desire for data and its unbridled data center growth while remaining a good steward of the environment?

The aforementioned diesel generator is one of the most intense focus areas these days. "Diesel Free by 2033" is a catchy expression of the desire to replace diesel generator technology at some of the largest facility builders and providers. Despite significant advances in diesel engine consumption and emission efficiency over the last 30+ years, the use of combustion engines has faced backlash for its carbon-based fuel system. However, in an emergency, the reliability of diesel engine systems is unparalleled.

Case in point, when the electrical grid collapsed in Texas during an unseasonable cold snap that grid engineers simply had not imagined and did not design for, data centers, hospitals, and EMS all rolled over to diesel generator backup power systems without a noticeable impact to services. So, despite the sustainability imperative, the roughly $8B global large diesel generator market is forecasted to continue growing by 7% per year because it simply works.[2]

As a data center provider though, it's a challenging time to design and operate infrastructure. Do we take up the sustainability mantle and push for innovation-fueled revolution; do we abandon carbon-based energy and go all-in on renewable sources, for example? Or do we preach the merits of evolution vis-à-vis six sigma continuous improvement, focusing on making existing infrastructure operations more efficient? The raising of hot aisle temperatures and thermal partitioning that many operators did ten years ago comes to mind. Picking the right direction and velocity can be daunting.

Fortunately, we are blessed to work in an industry that is filled with the most creative innovators on the planet *and* domain-master engineers who can optimize processes and push operating limits to the absolute edge to improve performance. We will both research, test, and deploy cutting edge new revolutionary replacement technologies and use our decades of proven field experience to inform operational advances to evolve existing practices.

Let's look at some of these approaches.

Revolutionary Sustainability

There's no better example of Schumpeter's Creative Destruction than what's going on inside of deep-pocketed, hyperscaler data centers' R&D labs. Revolutionary approaches to the source of power-inputs, or what the EPA, vis-à-vis emissions standards, refers to as scope 1 & 2. Both alternative fuels (hydrogen, utility-scale battery arrays) and power sources (wind, solar, even wave motion) are included here and have been the focus of advances in the last few years. The depth of research, development, and testing in this space is breathtaking. From Microsoft's progress with hydrogen to Google's pioneering work with batteries, we learn of exciting revolutionary advances seemingly monthly.

Hydrogen Fuel Cells

As diesel generators keep the bits flowing throughout hurricane seasons across the globe, no one is calling for the immediate demise of this proven solution. However, many hyperscalers have expressed a desire to move away from diesel. For example, Microsoft has demonstrated the viability of hydrogen fuel by running a small Azure environment with the technology. With engineers dedicating their intellectual prowess to creating a truly sustainable future and financial support from hyperscalers, the industry can count on demonstrable results. Once released to full-scale production environments, fuel cells represent a change to data center design, operations, purchasing, and supply chains that will be revolutionary for all involved.

The primary hurdle for the use of hydrogen fuel cells in data centers, or in any application, is the supply chain of green hydrogen. Green is the most desirable on the "color spectrum" of hydrogen as it is the only form of hydrogen produced with no greenhouse gas emissions. It is the only form of hydrogen suitable for fuel cell use.

Studies completed by Kohler show global hydrogen production today has a best-case carbon pollution of 355 g/kwh. Comparing this to the carbon pollution impact of diesel fuel of 293.6 g/kwh, we find that hydrogen as it stands today is not truly a clean solution or an ideal alternative to diesel fuel. It will be in the future though. As countries around the globe shift energy production sources from coal and natural gas to nuclear, hydro-electric, wind, and solar, green hydrogen production through electrolysis at scale will become a reality. In this case, hydrogen will produce as low as 6 g/kwh.

Production hurdles will be followed closely by the challenges of distribution and storage. Fossil-fuel distribution infrastructure took decades to grow to scale, and hydrogen will require the same growth period. Data centers will be a driving force given the massive corporations that back them, but the pace at which the shift occurs will also be dependent on many other factors such as on-road vehicle advancements, customer demand, and most notably, government regulation. While the timing is uncertain, we do know that green hydrogen will play a large role in a green future, not just for data centers, but for society as a whole.

Utility-Scale Batteries

The reason renewables are not yet viable as direct energy sources is because their output is based on the vagaries of Mother Nature and are highly variable. Therefore, to harness their energy we must be able to store it. But we do not yet have utility-scale battery capabilities as there are unsolved engineering challenges with sizing and scale.

Today the equivalent footprint of battery storage compared to a 3MW generator is 20:1. Using projections of Lithium-Ion battery technology, Kohler engineers project a capital cost double that of a diesel generator to run a facility for 24 hours. Considering the physical and economic constraints, along with the maintenance and reliability issues batteries are subject to, we believe battery storage will not be a direct replacement for diesel generators.

However, batteries enable us to rethink how a data center receives its power supply. As mentioned, batteries alleviate many of the issues facing grid-level renewables. Data centers could create local microgrids that provide primary power from renewables and are backed up by the electrical grid. Favorable opportunities are achievable, and we will continue to work with data center engineers to rethink the future of grid integration possibilities with all their power distribution equipment.

Sustainable Thinking

When thinking about solving challenges, we tend to focus on finite product and technology solutions. Engineers are particularly guilty of this. But some of the greatest advances often come from assessing entire systems, thinking about both the supply and demand side of the energy equation. Creative thinking that questions fundamental assumptions often yields the most effective results.

A great example is what Microsoft did a few years ago when designing their largest new data center in Chicago. Wrestling with how to drive PUE down by increasing operational efficiency, visionary leadership challenged the team to think not just about mechanical and electrical elements, but the entire IT delivery system, including server infrastructure. The result was an exponential advance in the delivery of critical load. Microsoft decided to eliminate the tedious process of server delivery and deployment by outsourcing this onerous and expensive task to server OEMs. To achieve this, they demanded that the servers be delivered racked, stacked, and cabled inside of a 40' shipping container.

Not only did this innovative approach remove significant time and cost from the IT pre-production phase, but also created an environment through which chilled air moved rapidly. Instead of trying to cool a small aisle in a large colocation hall—a process rife with inefficiencies- there were now four sides of a shipping container controlling cooling losses and facilitating thermal transfer. This LEGO® block approach to building data centers was truly revolutionary and resulted in what at the time was industry-leading PUE and the auxiliary sustainability benefit of driving OpEx down more than 30%. Inside the box thinking, some would say. Perhaps most importantly, with cost savings precedent set, revolutionary thinking took hold and fostered a culture of PUE-guided innovation. Designers and builders launched a 10-year run of modular approaches to facility construction whose legacy is still visible today.

Evolutionary Sustainability

Just as exciting is what's going on from an evolutionary perspective. No one is better at continuous improvement than the wonderfully Type-A critical environment operators behind the curtains at every facility. After running very complex large-scale facilities for many years with no unscheduled downtime, they've learned a few things about controlling entropy and have done so while simultaneously driving sustainability principles: use less power, use less water, optimize air flow, and so on. After years of this residual benefit, we're just now starting to see "sustainable operations": providers of data center operational services and equipment who align with the EPA's Scope 3 (outputs) are differentiating with Operations as a Service (OaaS).

As an analog, consider the success that Ford has had with their EcoBoost engine platform. By sizing the engine at a relatively paltry 3.6 liters, but twin-turbocharging it for periods of peak output, Ford achieved increases in both horsepower *and* MPG while dropping greenhouse emissions by 15%![3] In the generator space, Kohler is taking a similar evolutionary approach to sustainability. Like Ford, they have attacked the consumption side of the equation by questioning assumptions about traditional generator designs.

For decades, generators have been designed around a set of life-safety criteria, specifically, National Electric Code (NEC) and National Fire Protection Agency 110 Standard (NFPA 110). Rightfully so, these criteria demand quick and guaranteed response time in the event of an emergency. In a hospital, factory, apartment building, or school, it was assumed that electrical systems should be back online in ten seconds or less, with backup power distributed from a monolithic generator that supplied an entire standalone building.

With this set of life-safety, single-unit assumptions, standard operating procedures were developed that necessitated long, loaded, and frequent testing. This operations and maintenance (O&M) rigor resulted in exemplary failover response and success but gave no consideration to carbon impact. The unfortunate result of these O&M mandates in the data center space has been the operationalization of monthly fuel-burn and pollutant emissions.

Sustainable Engine Design

Aging engine technology hasn't helped. For decades, generator operators have had to mitigate the infamous "wet stacking" problem—the build-up of unburned fuel in the exhaust system. This unwanted residue accumulates when the generator runs at low load (generally under 30%) and does not reach a high enough temperature to seal the space between the pistons and cylinder walls and vaporize fuel that sneaks through. Besides reducing engine efficiency, wet-stacking decreases maintenance cycles and accelerates wear. It also interferes with emission control add-ons like diesel oxidation catalysts (DOC), selective catalyst reduction (SCR), and diesel particulate filters (DPF). Consequently, operators have learned over the years to run longer and at higher loads during tests to obviate wet stacking. The irony and tragedy of running generators longer, burning more fuel, and emitting greater pollutants, off of load banks, so that add-on technology meant to reduce carbon impact will function better should be lost on no one.

As with Ford's innovative approach to motor engine design, Kohler discarded the assumptions of the past and designed a generator engine specifically for data centers and with sustainability in mind. Their engineers beefed up gasketing and sealing, streamlined the fuel system, extended the lifetime of consumables, densified power, and virtually eliminated blow-by with precision piston assemblies. The result was astounding: a sustainable generator immune to wet-stacking. Instead of having to test monthly with load-simulation, data center operators can now test as little as once per year at low-load. Net fuel consumption reduction, conservatively, approaches 50% and emissions drop by over 80%.

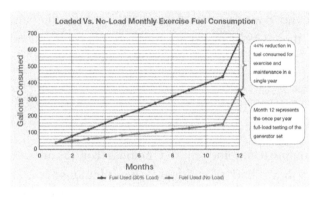

Loaded vs. no-load monthly exercise fuel
consumption

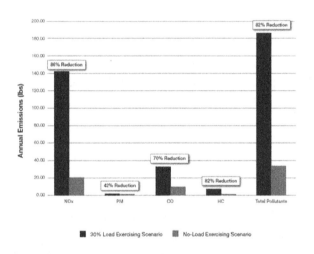

Loaded vs. no-load monthly exercise pollutant
creation

If these results were scaled across the global fleet of roughly 700 Hyperscale facilities, all operating 50 or more gensets, the reduction in carbon impact would get very real.

Reduced Emissions

Similarly, diesel generator manufacturers have been engineering hard since 2006 to meet the U.S. EPA emissions requirements for standby diesel generator engines. Over this period, pollutant emissions have been drastically curtailed. All standby generators in the U.S. now exceed EPA Tier 2 requirements. Kohler's redesigned engines, in addition to exceeding Tier 2 requirements, have remarkably low particulate matter emissions without requiring aftertreatment. Despite the advancements, Kohler has continued to battle against emitted pollutants through many initiatives, including the release of factory-direct Tier 4 packaged units. Our aftertreatment systems are the simplest in the industry, requiring only selective catalytic reduction technology to exceed Tier 4 limits. The result is a generator that emits 90% fewer pollutants than a similar generator would have just 15 years prior.

The advent of Tier 4 has also led to advancements in what is referred to as "compliant aftertreatment systems." They differ from factory packages because they use third-party supplier equipment and lack some advantages of fully integrated systems, but pollutant reduction results are similar. The wide range of pollutant abatement systems that data center operators can employ give them the ability to measure and herald these advances.

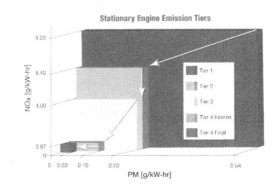

Stationary engine emission tiers

Green Fuel Alternatives

Another evolutionary advancement of diesel generators is renewable diesel fuels. Most notably HVO100 and R99 yield massive improvements to the carbon footprint of diesel generators. Renewable fuels utilize waste streams of vegetable oils and animal fats along with a process called hydrogenation to make superior diesel fuel when compared to traditional fossil diesel as well as traditional biodiesel made by esterification. The primary benefit of these fuels is a dramatic reduction in greenhouse gas emissions. Neste, a worldwide leader in renewable diesel production, reports a 90% reduction over the entire lifecycle of the fuel.

The other remarkable advantage of renewable fuels is stability. Traditional biodiesel degrades over time, making standby generator applications a poor fit for use. Renewables do not require frequent fuel polishing like traditional biodiesel. It was more likely for the fuel to go bad before ever being needed.

Renewable diesel is as stable as traditional fossil diesel while providing far superior advantages in greenhouse gas emissions. Further advantages are a dramatic reduction in smoke creation, and they can be used in existing diesel engines without any medication. Given the remarkable improvements, many data center operators are either already using or investigating the future use of renewable fuels.

Sustainable advancements of diesel engine and generator technology are set to accelerate. Data center applications will experience the greatest advancements. The combination of surging demand, end-user commitment to sustainable improvements, and limited life-safety regulations positions data centers as the focal segment for breakthrough advancements. The engineers at Kohler were quick to identify both the need and the opportunity.

Advancements are being made on all fronts as we innovate every aspect of standby power generation. Wide ranging advancements in fuels, consumables, operating plans, remote monitoring, and exhaust aftertreatment create endless opportunities to improve diesel engines. Data center IT load constitutes the largest demand for large displacement diesel engines in the world. All stakeholders are committed to change: with collaboration and ingenuity, we can build a sustainable evolution as revolutionary solutions mature.

It's useful to use this context when thinking about the next chapter in data center sustainability measurement. PUE hasn't become passe, but thanks to increased measurement capabilities across the entire data center sustainability value chain, it now feels unidimensional. As an example, NTT Data Centers recently produced an advert that included a facility-specific breakdown of utility power generation source – gas, solar, wind, nuclear, coal, etc. This granularity is both impressive and a strong demand signal for multivariate measurement.

Conclusion

Kohler believes in a better planet, better communities, and better lives. Therefore, we are committed to sustainability in the data center space and are pursuing both revolutionary and evolutionary products and solutions on our journey to better. We know it won't be easy to solve sustainability challenges, but our vision of the future includes data center generators that leverage optimized and efficient diesel and after-treatment systems and radical new approaches to backup power systems like utility-scale batteries and hydrogen fuel cells which challenge established norms.

We at Kohler are proud of our accomplishments, but we always believe we can do better. Kohler's vision is to power future data needs more efficiently, reliably, and sustainably. This ethos has inspired innovation and gracious customer experience since 1873 and manifests in our relentless focus on doing better, forcing us to continually think differently to address societal and environmental issues. Solving them is not necessarily easy, but we can come together as an industry to share success and failures, thereby embracing what we learn to drive change for a better future.

1. Kohler internal research.

2. Danielle, S. 2021. "What to Know about the Ford EcoBoost Engines." Vehicle-History. March 4, 2021. https://www.vehiclehistory.com/articles/what-to-know-about-the-ford-ecoboost-engines.

3. Polit, Kate. 2021. "EPA Expands Efforts to Improve Energy Efficiency of U.s. Data Centers." MeriTalk. September 15, 2021. https://www.meritalk.com/articles/epa-expands-efforts-to-improve-energy-efficiency-of-u-s-data-centers/.

About the Author

SEAN FARNEY

A recovering data center operator who built and ran a 120MW facility, Sean Farney is still an industry nerd and now runs marketing for Kohler Data Centers, the data center industry's Global Power Partner. Past roles include Founder of Ubiquity Critical Environments, Data Center Manager at Microsoft, and Head of Data Center Operations at 7ticks, a high-frequency trading start-up now part of ICE. Today, he also manifests his industry love by teaching a course on technology-infused culture and the important role that data centers play at his alma mater, Northwestern University.

About the Author

BRAD MEISSNER

Brad Meissner manages the entire product line for Kohler Data Centers, and is the company's resident expert in emissions, sustainability, and EPA codes & compliance. As a power systems engineer, he's worked on everything from alternators and diesel fuel tanks to enclosure systems—and even a solar ATS to help support developing nations' water filtration systems. Through his work, Brad continues to actively seek new ways to drive sustainability across the data center ecosystem.

About the Author

MELISSA REALI-ELLIOTT

As a self-professed data center nerd, Melissa revels in promoting Kohler products and services as their Digital & Social Marketing Manager. With 15 years of industry experience, including a stint running the data center segment marketing for ABB, she's adept at mission critical marketing, branding, and messaging.

FIVE

Patrick Giangrosso

THE ROAD TO SUSTAINABILITY

When I think of the future, I look at it through the lens of parenthood. I think about the promises, both spoken and not, that I've made to set my children up for the best possible future I can provide. While those promises include the typical things like access to education and a stable home with a roof over their heads, I also like to think about the bigger picture, including the planet that I leave for them. I remember going on Y-Guides outings with my daughters and telling them that we always leave the place we visit better than when we found it. We are only visiting this home we call Earth. I'm confident that I'm not alone in my line of thought. The world is full of parents who are looking toward the future of the planet for their children and for generations to come. Even for those who aren't parents, we all have concerns about the groundwork we are laying for a sustainable future.

The power of the word "sustainable" continues to grow, and trends and initiatives fluctuate as leaders look to take action and affect change. The drive to be green and sustainable is driven by organizations looking to increase their Environmental, Social, and Governance (ESG) score. Whatever the reason, the desired result is laudable. Unfortunately, being sustainable and achieving sustainable practices are not as simple as your intent to do so. You'd be hard-pressed to find a recent headline that didn't include mention of some sort of sustainability initiative that is promised to be the focus of a company's efforts in the next few years. While intending to make change is commendable, it often isn't enough for those visions to come to fruition, particularly when you consider the lack of standardization in the data center industry. To put it simply, many are making the claim, but few are delivering on those promises. This isn't due to a lack of effort; instead, it's the result of the slow standardization efforts across the industry, acceptance of proven technologies, and implementation industry-wide.

A Bumpy Path Ahead

It is no secret that the data center industry has not implemented many environmentally sustainable solutions. While many are starting to plan for the potential implementation of more sustainable practices, the reality is that data centers in their current state are incredibly energy-intensive. In fact, research conducted at energy.gov puts any given data center's energy consumption at roughly 10 to 50 times that of a similar-sized "regular" office building.[1] Data centers are also in higher demand than ever before as the world continues to become more digitized. From a significant increase in remote work and AI to the rise in cryptocurrency mining (which tends to consume extreme amounts of energy), more and more data centers are being built in order to support those needs. On the surface, this may not sound like a negative trend, especially for those of us in the industry. Truthfully, it's just the reality of the world we live in. That's not to say the industry isn't already recognizing the need for a change to sustainable data center practices.

I would argue that there we have already seen a small shift starting with the creation of Power Usage Effectiveness (PUE). The Green Grid Group, a group of industry leaders, created the

PUE to drive others toward efficiency, and as a result, helped the industry take its first step toward less energy usage.

As data centers continue to be built to meet rising demand, the question of how to get "greener" data into major cities has already been asked and many are working toward finding that answer. The need for sustainable technology in our cities is here. What is lacking is the infrastructure itself, in part, due to the uphill economic battle that accompanies significant change.

To be blunt, the companies willing to invest in sustainable operations and centers are not the majority. As it stands today, they are few and far between. While the intent and desire might be there 'when push comes to shove', many are faced with an economic commitment that they are both unwilling and unable to make. Whenever you are at the front end of change, the price is often hefty. We are early in the stages of the maturity cycle, which means there is a higher cost. It truly becomes an investment and a commitment of resources because the money you pay now will take time to show a financial return on your balance sheet. Even though it might be a worthy investment that results in positive change down the road, those who can make that investment early on are the exception. Accepting that economic commitment and getting buy-in are two of the significant hurdles we face as we look toward a more sustainable future.

A major deterrent preventing any company from investing upfront is the trickle-down costs that will make their way down to their customers. After all, part of the way to recoup your investment is to pass some of that cost to the customer level. If customers aren't willing to pay for a sustainable solution, though, there is a risk of losing income. Because of this, the buy-in that the industry ultimately needs to see real change extends its reach all the way to the customer level. Customers must be willing to pay a higher price for that sustainable service, and they must believe in the benefits they are paying for that higher price. The market needs to be willing to pay a higher price for the "sustainable" service, just as customers are willing to pay a higher price for organic food. Companies should be financially rewarded for successful sustainability efforts.

In addition, companies need to be open to exploring and accepting new technologies that will drive sustainability, such as solar, hydrogen, and others that are environmentally friendly and less detrimental than traditional methods of operation. Traditionally, the acceptance of new technologies in the data center has been slow. However, as we have seen with the introduction of the PUE, the adoption of new technologies can come quickly when agreed metrics are the end objective.

Speaking of buy-in, the final bill isn't the only speed bump we're facing. While one company might be ready to take the expense and commit to a sustainable build, to be truly sustainable, every partner involved in that process must also hold the same commitment. Each vendor and partner in a supply chain must be willing to take on the same expense and make the same commitment to ensure their operations are sustainable from start to finish. While growing, the concept of sustainable operations is still far from the standard, which means finding partners who share the same level of commitment will not be an easy feat—at least not this early in the game. There will need to be a shift in the community mindset to increase the number of companies committed to the same goals and practices to support a truly sustainable data center. This means one of the first challenges the industry faces is to recognize that the issue of sustainability is important and agree to minimize the impact through a complete change.

As "Easy as 1, 2, 3"...

If we know there's a need, and we know the challenges we will face to get there, the next logical question is "How do we get there?" At the risk of minimizing the work ahead, I see three general yet crucial steps in the path to greener data:

1. **The industry needs to standardize what it means to be "sustainable."** The truth is there is

still a great deal of mystery surrounding sustainability that makes it difficult to verify the authenticity of the claims that some are making. How can we know we're sustainable without knowing what sustainable really means and/or looks like? Until the industry establishes clear guidelines and criteria that a data center—and its vendors—must meet to be classified as sustainable, we will continue to see marketing-based claims that are surface-level tactics at best and "green-washing" at worst. Standardizing the definitions of sustainability as they apply to data centers isn't just helpful for weeding out false narratives in the market either. These standards and definitions help guide those looking to become sustainable to know whether they are making the right changes and provide a blueprint and set of metrics by which their performance and success can be measured and adjusted. Furthermore, this can help us understand where the gaps are and how to close them. For example, I might have every intention of being a more environmentally-friendly data center, but if I have my building materials delivered via a container ship that runs on diesel fuel, am I technically 100% sustainable? Is the carbon footprint left by that single vendor enough to negate some of the other steps I'm taking? Would that answer have changed depending on who I bought those materials from? This may seem like going down the rabbit hole a bit, but it's that game of 20-questions that our industry needs to play in order to define what sustainability means in our space so that we can do our best to hit that mark. Just like in the mid-2000s when the Green Grid Group developed the PUE, we need a governing organization that will develop metrics that the community can agree on. This way, there is a method to measure, monitor, and prove a company's level of sustainability.

2. **Identify a clear path.** Once we've established what

it takes to be sustainable, we must examine what that path looks like for everyone. After all, if we were all able to flip the switch and make the necessary changes now, we'd be a lot further along in this discussion. To ensure more companies and data centers can make the shift, we need to establish measurable goals and ensure that the necessary technologies to bridge any gaps are available. The path will likely resemble a "crawl, walk, run" approach with many setting more straightforward goals like being a certain percentage more sustainable each year over year. Small changes now will add up to significant results over time. Being 100% sustainable is not likely a metric that every data center will reach quickly. Instead, we can establish how to measure sustainability in a way that incentivizes smaller, more achievable goals to be set that eventually lead to that 100% mark. If 100% isn't possible for your center in the next year, maybe a more realistic option would be to hit 70% sustainable operations (as established by the industry standard) and increase the rating by 5% each year over the last. Incremental movement is still movement. The way to make any movement possible is by establishing a standard by which to measure and a set of metrics to track progress. Otherwise, we are all moving blindly in a dark room, hoping we happen to find a light switch.

3. **Incentivize, incentivize, incentivize.** Half the battle is knowing what we want to achieve and how we will achieve it. The other half? Get everyone to walk that path with you. At the simplest of levels, the expenditure—in terms of money, effort, and energy—needs to be worth it for those involved. The environmental benefits will undoubtedly be enough for some. There will be others, however, that are looking for more measurable and immediate returns. A different set of motivation factors doesn't lessen the

potential impact. If the goal is to foster a sustainable industry standard, we should look to involve as many stakeholders as possible, regardless of what motivates them to take the desired action. Providing incentives helps widen the net we cast to capture the attention of those that might otherwise have not considered going green. End-users should be willing to pay more for a more sustainable data center.

Leading The Way

I know what you're thinking—"it's easy to sit behind a keyboard and tell the world what they need to be doing." At least, that's what I'd be thinking if *I* were on the other side of the screen. My simple answer would be to say that my team and I are doing our best to practice what I (unintentionally) preach.

My experience in the industry has allowed me to witness these efforts first-hand long before today's sustainability movement. I started in the early 2000s developing fuel cell projects to help clients reduce their carbon emissions (back before being sustainable was cool). I've been able to watch customers and partners alike take high-level ideas of sustainability and eco-friendly operations and mold them into tactics for their clients. What once sounded like an unattainable dream has been explained and explored until real-life applications were discovered. Once the opportunity is identified, it's simply a matter of developing the solution.

What that means for my team and me is that understanding the high level allows us to think about what services and solutions we are bringing to our clients and how we can improve them to fill any gaps. Our team aims to look at that bigger picture and translate those ideas into practical applications that are relevant to our industry, market, and customers. This top-to-bottom approach has already proven to be useful for us.

One of the largest changes we've been able to make, for example, has been our utilization of sustainable technologies and solutions that, in turn, provide our customers with more sustainable options. We've developed a microgrid and modular data center solution that steer away from using diesel generators using entirely solar-powered primary energy with fuel cell and green hydrogen as a backup. We do this while utilizing partners and vendors that provide recycled and sustainable solutions as well. We've surrounded ourselves with like-minded individuals who allow us to commit fully to our sustainable solutions so that our customers can rest easy knowing they have a truly sustainable option. And while we can't force anyone to use those solutions, we can make them available. We can provide those practical solutions that serve both the needs of our customers while also serving the needs of the environment.

Big Changes Start Small

The data center industry has a reputation for being slow-moving in acceptance of new technologies and practices. While this has been the case historically, it doesn't have to be. Over the past five years, data center cooling went from traditional CRAC and CRAH to Adiabatic and free air cooling, a shift that was relatively fast-moving in its adoption when compared to past technologies. Data centers have rapidly accepted the transformerless UPS with high energy efficiency as the de facto standard. The reason? PUE. Companies saw how this cooling enabled them to get a low PUE and how they could help operations as a result. In other words, there were measurable results that incentivized companies to take advantage. The sustainable data initiative can be the same if we provide the metrics to measure themselves against and leapfrog into the technologies to help them achieve those desired metrics.

One of the biggest opportunities I see for achieving more sustainable data lies in establishing peer groups to lead the way. Our peers can be some of the most persuasive and compelling individuals and seeing those around us unite toward any cause often compels us to join in the conversation. Organizations like the Green Grid Group are real examples of the power in numbers. Not only are those groups starting those important conversations, but they also move beyond discussion to provide tools and resources for others looking to achieve the same mission. From establishing the standards and definitions I mentioned earlier to providing support and guidance along the way, it will ultimately take the combined efforts of those forward-thinking individuals to lead our industry down the sustainability path we are all seeking.

I look at the entire sustainable data conversation first as a father—a father who has promised his children the best possible future I can provide. My daughters and I have had many discussions about what we feel is our responsibility to leave a given space in better condition than we found it. It's a philosophy that, although simple, is one I find to be incredibly valuable and one that I consider in all things I do. I wholeheartedly believe that part of the future I set up for my daughters involves leaving the planet in a better condition than I found it. And while I may not be able to force my customers or peers into being 100% sustainable, I can still keep my word to my daughters, which is this:

> I promise to do all I can to offer sustainable options and solutions, even if I'm the only one asking for them. I promise to continue finding and working with like-minded individuals who see the value in leaving the planet in better condition for future generations. I promise to do things like join groups and write chapters in books and be a part of the discussion in any way I can. Most of all, I promise to leave my space in the industry better than when I found it.

---

1. Energy.gov. 2022. "Data Centers and Servers." Energy.gov. https://www.energy.gov/eere/buildings/data-centers-and-servers.

About the Author

PATRICK GIANGROSSO

Patrick Giangrosso is the Vice President at Mission Critical Facilities International (MCFI). At MCFI, he manages full life cycle solutions for data center and cooling infrastructures around the world, the implementation of MCFI's GENIUS Modular Data Centers and MicroGENIUS, a solar/fuel cell microgrid solution delivering sustainable, efficient, grid-independent energy.

For more than two decades, Patrick has developed and managed mission critical telecom channel relationships and initiatives in the U.S., China, India, Latin America, and Europe. Drawing upon his background as an Electrical Engineer/MBA, Patrick is driven to provide the best solution to help customers—from executives to end-users—achieve their goals. Before joining MCFI, he held global sales and engineering leadership roles at Jacobs Engineering, Coolcentric, Liebert, GE, Eaton Corporation, and IBM.

Patrick's areas of expertise include Mission Critical Infrastructure, Project Development, Power Generation (Gas Turbines, Fuel Cells, and Micro-Turbines), Project Management, Technical/Capital Intensive Solution Sales, and Solution Development. Patrick lives in Raleigh, North Carolina, with his wife and two daughters.

SIX

Kim Gunnelius

THE JOURNEY TO DARK GREEN–AND BEYOND

While many business leaders are putting greater emphasis on understanding sustainability—there appears to be a gap between knowing about its importance and doing something to attain it. A study by Boston Consulting Group,[1] in collaboration with MIT, found that whereas 90 percent of executives find sustainability to be important, only 60 percent of companies incorporate sustainability in their strategy, and just 25 percent have sustainability incorporated in their business model. This "knowing-versus-doing gap," illustrates how, although companies recognize the need to act on sustainability, too few are doing so.

Today, the heat is on for companies around the world to reduce their carbon footprint, and the temperature will continue to rise as customers, suppliers, and stakeholders increase the pressure to go green. Now is the time for corporate leaders to take notice and realize that good intentions are no longer enough. It is time to act.

Our Story

When we founded Ficolo in 2011, it was important to us to use 100 percent green energy from day one. This didn't happen because we watched what other companies were doing and followed suit; it happened because we took action. A green business is a sustainable business that has no negative impact on the global or local environment, community, society, or economy. We knew that was the type of business we wanted Ficolo to be, and our business plan was built around that mission.

As a result, we've taken a different path that sets us apart from many digital infrastructure companies. When it became apparent that innovative data center services were needed in the Nordics, we saw an opportunity to embark on something groundbreaking, and we became the first company to bring colocation services to Finland. However, instead of building traditional data centers, we established our first operation in an underground network of tunnels originally dug by the Finnish defense forces. We recognized the fortuitous opportunity to capitalize on the cool Nordic climate and the bedrock's built-in security and natural cooling capabilities, and we jumped on it.

Many companies are looking to be carbon neutral in five, ten, or even fifteen years down the road. Ficolo is there now. In 2019, we received climate research institute Cicero's highest rating of Dark Green, becoming the first and only data center in the world to have earned this rating. Ficolo also holds the Climate Neutral Company Certification granted by Swiss carbon finance consultancy, South Pole. After only ten years, Ficolo is now the second-largest colocation provider in Finland. Our growth, coupled with achieving net-zero carbon emissions, is validation that sustainability and business can—and should—go hand in hand.

However, we're not stopping at being climate neutral; we are pushing the envelope on sustainability, and our ultimate goal is to be carbon negative.

Together as a Global Industry, We Can Create Greener Data

While every company is positioned differently, each one has the opportunity to identify available resources and align them with environmental priorities to develop a holistic sustainability strategy. This will help companies make realistic decisions on resourcing and strategizing around the issues that matter to their business. Capitalizing on natural resources such as solar energy, wind energy, hydroelectricity, and geothermal energy moves them further and faster down the road to becoming carbon neutral.

Allocating resources to improve sustainability is not a cost—it's an investment. Environmentally- progressive initiatives that were once viewed as financial trade-offs are now considered innovative business strategies. As an industry, we have the potential to radically drive progress in the global effort against climate change.

In this chapter, I hope to share our experience to help others establish the mindset and principles to embark on their own successful journey to climate neutrality—and beyond.

As individuals, most of us take steps to live more sustainably. Undoubtedly however, most of the global greenhouse gas emissions are produced by industries. In the corporate world, this should be viewed not as a challenge, but as an opportunity. As business leaders, we have an intrinsic perspective on what is required for our businesses' day-to-day operations. We can use this insight and our expertise to develop a holistic sustainability strategy that benefits not only the environment, but also our companies, our customers, and the industry as a whole. This is the foundation upon which Ficolo was built.

The journey to achieve climate neutrality presents some obstacles, but every step, big or small, takes an operation closer to reaching this goal. For example, identifying specific emissions sources and assessing the effects of each is an important step in developing a sustainability plan, but it is not an easy task. Everything from construction components, to hardware and travel requirements to the smallest office supplies must be considered. The process is compounded by the fact that a company's carbon footprint is also proportional to emissions across the entire supply chain. Because of this, corporate leaders must have their finger on the pulse of the environmental contributions of their suppliers, partners, and vendors, in addition to their own.

The sheer magnitude of it all might be part of the reason that, instead of rolling up their sleeves and pushing the initiative to become climate neutral forward today, many companies have instead made it a long-term goal. Or maybe the substantiality of infrastructure investments, combined with the significant footprint of equipment and components factor into why companies are looking to be carbon neutral in five, ten, or even fifteen years down the road. They want to get there, but the roadblocks are hard to overlook, holding the operation back when it should be preparing to move forward.

Before taking on an initiative as sophisticated as climate neutrality, corporate leaders must first define the process they will take to get there. According to the Carbon Disclosure Project, (CDP) some of the primary barriers that organizations face when setting environmental action goals include: uncertainty about where to begin, lack of data reporting, budgetary issues, and lack of support from stakeholders.[4] Additional challenges include internal misalignment and fear of failure. Once an organization has set their goals for reaching net zero, they face even further challenges, such as with many citing an unclear plan of action.

Recognize Climate Neutrality as a Business Advantage

As recently as 10 years ago, climate neutrality was barely a topic of discussion. Five years ago it became a bit more interesting, and then recently, we started seeing "certified climate neutral" in RFPs as one of the top requirements. Additionally, due to stricter policies and goals resulting from the Paris Agreement, businesses that don't take action may start to experience a decreased demand for their products and services, in conjunction with a rise in CO2 emissions costs. As such, these businesses will have lower margins, and could see up to 50 percent of their profits put at risk.[2]

A climate neutral certification gives businesses a competitive advantage. Cloud services have a significant environmental impact, and customers know that. Worldwide, data centers use around two percent of all the electricity produced, and this figure is estimated to rise to eight percent by the end of the decade.[3] Companies that want to procure cloud services care about their environmental footprint reputation, and they will turn to a cloud service provider who is committed to carbon-neutral operations. However, for many large organizations, it's about more than just climate neutrality—it also comes back to costs.

The most impactful cost savings that customers in this industry see as a result of climate-friendly initiatives is in relation to electricity. As much as 75 percent of a pure-play data center's operational costs are spent on energy. For providers that optimize data center energy consumption, power costs are much lower, thus dramatically reducing customers' power costs.

Companies often debate whether sustainability undermines or improves financial results. According to research by non-profit organization CDP, companies who diligently plan and manage climate change are able to gain an 18 percent higher return on investment than businesses that do not.[4] Additionally, companies have seen their sustainable products grow 5.6 times faster than non-sustainable products.[5] Clearly, corporate leaders need to start thinking about the green initiative as an investment in their future and stop seeing it as cutting into the bottom line.

Take the First Step—Examine the Scope of Emissions

Carbon emissions are responsible for 81% of overall GHG emissions,[6] and businesses are responsible for most of that. On our path to becoming climate neutral, we examined the scope of emissions[7] as defined by the GHG Protocol:

> *Scope one emissions* are the direct emissions that your activities create—for instance, the exhaust from the trucks a company

uses to transport its products from one place to another or the generators it might run.

Scope two emissions are indirect emissions that come from the production of the electricity or heat you use, like the traditional energy sources that power a business' buildings.

Scope three emissions are the indirect emissions that come from all the other activities.

For a business, these emission sources can be extensive and must be accounted for across its entire supply chain, the materials in its buildings, the business travel of its employees, and the full life cycle of its products, including the electricity customers may consume when using the product. Given this broad range, a company's scope for all three emissions are often far larger than its scope one and two emissions combined.

Most companies have been focusing their efforts on scopes one and two, over which they have more control. However, there is a growing need to direct our sights on scope three emissions, which account for several times the impact of scopes one and two emissions. This is why it is critical for business leaders aiming for carbon neutrality to understand the impact of their supply chain in addition to their infrastructure's energy efficiency. In addition to only using IT equipment from suppliers with sustainable supply chain policies, we also have a strict recycling policy and require ISO 14,000 certificates from our waste disposal partners.

Consider These 7 Guiding Principles to Set a Path Towards Greener Data

From day one, Ficolo has been committed to increasing energy efficiency and establishing its position as the global market leader in terms of sustainable innovation. Ficolo introduced a comprehensive environmental policy in tandem with the launch of the company based on these seven guiding principles:

1. **Seek out 100 percent green energy.** From

renewable electricity generated by wind turbines to using solar power plants for cooling during the higher-temperature summer months, seek out green energy sources available in your data center location.

2. **Optimize conditions for energy efficient processes.** One such way is to use Power Usage Effectiveness ratio (PUE). PUE is the ratio between the total energy consumption and the energy consumption by the data center's IT equipment. Using this method, Ficolo has not only optimized the energy consumption of the data centers we construct, but we also improve the energy efficiency of the data centers we acquire. Acquired data centers are selected, in part, based on energy efficiency improvement potential, and energy usage is converted to 100 percent green energy immediately.

3. **Establish cold and hot aisles utilizing free cooling**. This can be achieved through a modular structure, which means that only the area in active use needs to be cooled. In addition to using modular structures, Ficolo uses extremely efficient free cooling, which means we capitalize on our region's naturally cool air rather than using mechanical refrigeration.

4. **Recycle all waste.** Focus on keeping waste at minimum, particularly landfill waste, and pay extra attention to the recycling of electronic waste. Ficolo also pays careful attention to the amount of waste its operations produce as a byproduct. By far the largest source of waste is data center equipments' packing materials. In response, we procure our equipment only from reputable suppliers with strict sustainable supply chain policies and certifications inclusive of both packing materials and the equipment itself, including manufacturing, logistics, and energy efficiency.

5. **Support your customers' environmental awareness by providing them the exact figures**

of their energy consumption. Our data centers' electricity usage is monitored and optimized in real time. Ficolo's customers have access to the customer portal where they can monitor their servers' workload and electricity usage, as well as the associated cost. This effectively increases customers' awareness of their electricity consumption associated with data storage and processing. Real-time monitoring of electricity usage also enables Ficolo to react to abnormal peaks in electricity usage on a customer and a server level.

6. **Value products that help to protect the environment and utilize energy-efficient technology.** Pay careful attention to the amount of waste your operations produce as a byproduct. As noted above, we procure our IT equipment only from reputable suppliers with strict sustainable supply chain policies and certifications in place. Further, Ficolo recycles all waste it produces to minimize landfill waste.

7. **Reuse waste heat.** Equip your data centers with heat recovery to utilize the waste heat in the data center facility or local remote heating networks. Data center operations generate heat that can be reused instead of pushed out into the atmosphere. Ficolo The Air, our newest data center, utilizes waste heat recovery and distributes the surplus heat to a district heating system where recycled heat can be used to deliver heating for local housing. This exploits the green energy a second time and further reduces emissions. We are then able to reuse waste heat by selling it back to the energy company.

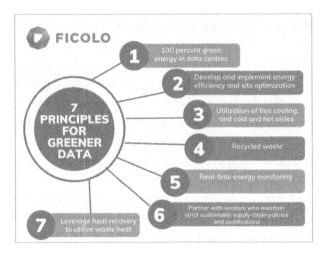

Push Past Neutral to Go Beyond Dark Green

In 2020, less than one percent of Ficolo's emissions came from scopes one and two as defined by the GHG Protocol, and all emissions were compensated. Now, the next steps are clear—we need to focus on scope three and on maximizing our handprint to achieve a carbon-negative status. As defined by the VTT Technical Research Center in Finland, "carbon handprint" describes a company's positive climate impacts. The idea behind the carbon handprint is that the company develops products and services that allow its customers to also reduce their carbon footprint. The bigger the handprint, the better.

We have already taken several actions to maximize our handprint, such as waste heat recovery, using 100 percent green energy, and helping our customers to eliminate emissions for their data centers, by outsourcing to us. And although these steps are notable, we know there is a lot more that can be done to reduce our carbon impact. A few of the initiatives we are looking at for the future include sustainable concrete, replacing diesel with green energy, and working with our customers to help them find channels to reuse their equipment.

Companies that have reached carbon neutrality are faced with their own set of challenges. We experienced such challenges on our journey, and still encounter them today in some cases. For example, Ficolo has been certified climate neutral, but as we're thinking about climate negativity, there are no set standards in place to measure what carbon-negative means. A universal method or framework to calculate and verify carbon negativity would be a huge step toward closing the gap between corporations' commitments and them taking action to attain carbon neutrality and, eventually, carbon negativity. Without an international standard, there is no true-negative. During a recent roundtable, however, I mentioned the idea of handing the responsibility of establishing this framework over to the European Union. To this, the moderator cautioned me to "be careful what you wish for," because any set standards need to be adequately monitored and regulated. Meaning, if the framework is too rigid, it will be difficult, if not impossible, to regulate and for companies to comply. In light of this, there needs to be balance within the framework.

Closing Thoughts

Every company has its own unique story, and every company's journey to achieve net zero and beyond carbon emissions is different. Our customers and sustainability are at the heart of Ficolo's operations, guiding our decisions. Therefore, we understand that now is the time to move forward, to explore better solutions and create change.

By combining business, mindset, and execution, we all can achieve carbon neutrality and become agents of change for our customers and our planet — strengthening the reputation of our distinguished industry and enhancing our collective positive impact.

---

1. Haanaes, Knut. 2016. "Why All Businesses Must Embrace Sustainability and Lead the Way." IMD Business School. November 4, 2016. https://www.imd.org/research-knowledge/articles/why-all-businesses-should-embrace-sustainability/.

2. Ruf, Yvonne, and David Frans. 2021. "Climate Action: A New Competitiveness Paradigm." Roland Berger. April 19, 2021. https://www.rolandberger.com/en/Insights/Publications/Climate-action-A-new-competitiveness-paradigm.html.

3. Ficolo. 2021. "Climate Neutrality." Ficolo. April 13, 2021. https://www.ficolo.com/climate-neutral/stable-environment/.

4. Labutong, Nicole and Vincent Hoen. 2018. "How can companies address their scope 3 greenhouse gas emissions?" SDP.Net. July 13, 2018. https://www.cdp.net/en/articles/companies/how-can-companies-address-their-scope-3-greenhouse-gas-emissions.

5. Planetly. 2021. "5 Reasons Why Your Company Should Become Carbon Neutral." Planetly. March 31, 2021. https://www.planetly.com/articles/5-reasons-why-your-company-should-become-carbon-neutral.

6. United States Environmental Protection Agency. n.d. "Overview of Greenhouse Gases." EPA.gov. https://www.epa.gov/ghgemissions/overview-greenhouse-gases.

7. Bernoville, Tara. 2020. "What Are Scopes 1, 2 and 3 of Carbon Emissions?" Plan A Academy. August 12, 2020. https://plana.earth/academy/what-are-scope-1-2-3-emissions/.

About the Author

KIM GUNNELIUS

As CCO and co-founder of Ficolo, Kim drives the marketing and international sales of Ficolo's climate neutral certified data center services. Having overseen the startup and growth phase of Ficolo as Chairman, Kim joined Ficolo full time in 2017 as CCO. In his position, he identifies and manages opportunities globally, ranging from Hyperscale and HPC to enterprise, including working with the largest technology companies in the world. He also oversaw the green certification initiatives that helped Ficolo achieve several industry firsts, such as the first Dark Green rated green bond for a data center company as well as the first hyperscale-level, climate neutral certification for a Nordic data center.

Having reached carbon neutrality in 2021, many years ahead of competing companies' targets, Ficolo is advancing towards a carbon negative, climate-positive operation. Under Kim's leadership, Ficolo efforts include reusing excess heat into the district heating grid to create a positive handprint in addition to a zero footprint.

With a background in software and telecom, Kim has helped build the financial foundation at Ficolo and define its position as one of the top data centers in Finland and an internationally recognized, sustainable leader in Colocation.

SEVEN

Lee Kirby

SUSTAINABILITY–THE APEX OF OPERATIONAL EXCELLENCE

The rapid growth of digital infrastructure to support the global economy has driven an ever-increasing demand for natural resources. This development adds to human-induced climate change. At the current rate of growth and consumption, it is unfathomable what the carbon footprint trend will look like in 5-10 years if we, as leaders in the data center industry, do not change our behaviors now. As an industry, we must do our part to protect and sustain the environment. Innovation and emerging technologies will proliferate the advancement of energy efficiency but conservation initiatives are advancing at a slow rate. Whether you are in the newest, most efficiently designed and built data center or in a legacy site, how you operate the site is critical to sustainability and profitability. Especially since an IDC survey found that almost 9 out of 10 data centers are not designed for optimal power efficiency,[1] which, as a result, can cost a data center more than $1.4 million every year in wasted electricity, based on national averages.

The key to sustainability for the life cycle of a data center is operations. A poor operations strategy can make the newest, most efficiently designed and built data center run inefficiently and world-class operations can maximize the efficiency of a legacy data center. Understanding that operational excellence cannot be separated from sustainability is the key point that will help you craft a highly effective operations program. In my chapter, I will lay out the building blocks for operational excellence.

Making a Sustainable Difference in Your Facility

It is our social responsibility to help data centers efficiently transition to more sustainable practices as an industry. There are five building blocks to consider as you develop your operations program:

1. Workforce Development
2. Resource Optimization
3. Sustainability Road Map, Measurements & Goal Setting
4. Methodical Audits
5. Local Requirements

The key is to take a holistic approach that encompasses the life cycle of the data center and drives efficiencies to all systems, processes, and teams with the understanding that change will be constant and focused on continuous improvement. Without an operating model that encompasses the points above with measurable and methodical processes, it will be impossible to get the full benefit of sustainable operations.[2] Moreover, investing in an Environmental, Social and Governance (ESG) rating is a vital part of an analysis process that identifies risks and growth opportunities by measuring a company's exposure to long-term environmental risks. Congruently, incorporating a data center lifecycle analysis (LCA) helps make more informed decisions regarding design and operational activities that contribute to and can reduce a data center's environmental impact.

5 Steps to Becoming a Sustainable Operator

Step 1: Workforce Development

After 36 years in the Army, I realized that basic training was just the starting point to prepare me for a journey of learning and growth throughout my career. We built Salute Mission Critical similarly, and by unleashing the power of the workforce, we have outperformed expectations in all categories. The key to sustainable operations starts with the workforce.

It is essential to resource, train and incentivize the workforce to embed elements of sustainability across all job functions. A sustainable workforce results from an organization's emphasis on culture and programs that support employee wellbeing. For example, providing hybrid or work-from-home opportunities and reducing travel can be important factors in reducing indirect carbon footprint while promoting a healthy work/life balance.

Sustainability especially thrives in organizations where the culture encourages creativity and innovation, aside from an employee's ability to complete the day-to-day demands of their position. These environments look beyond mere job training to continuous learning, empowerment, and the development of employees to build loyalty, resilience and a collaborative spirit that works to achieve the organization's vision and goals.

It also challenges employees to grow at an accelerated pace through specific, measurable, achievable, realistic and time-based (SMART) goals and stretch targets to improve business performance and maximize employee unity. In parallel, top to bottom commitment will incentivize senior leadership to maintain a formal and coordinated oversight of material and salient sustainable business priorities, held accountable by the board via compensation packages tied to sustainability goals.

In the military and at Salute Mission Critical a diverse workforce has proven to be a force multiplier. Diversity is a strength within the company's values and culture. It drives innovation and performance as you unleash the aggregate talent of a wide range of experiences and perspectives. Creating a culture that accepts people will cascade into an experience that encourages diverse opinions and ideas in a collaborative/positive environment versus a confrontational, subservient, and begrudging manner.

Inclusive environments result in greater emotional intelligence and the development of skills to address diverse situations. An emotionally intelligent culture is one where employees feel psychologically safe at work; they can be themselves and voice their opinions, innovations and ideas for improvement. A diverse and inclusive workplace builds better strategies, is better prepared to solve problems and overcome challenges. It creates an environment where employees support and rally together around the organization's goals.

This first step is the platform that will drive the innovation and performance cycles required to deliver optimal sustainable operations. A highly trained diverse workforce will naturally drive greater outcomes and prove the key to sustainable operations.

Step 2: Resource Optimization

As they relate to sustainability, resources include people and materials (raw materials to make goods, plants, animals, coal, natural gas, and oil to produce energy). To adequately grasp the scope of this vital area, it helps to separate between people and materials.

The first area to focus on is people and understanding the importance of their role and the outcome of optimizing. The variables in people optimization are capacity, demand, utilization and time. Optimization is finding the most efficient and sustainable use of the variables. Prioritizing work across a pool of people will help put the right people with the right skills at the right time. By managing and prioritizing the work this way, an organization will have a good view of capacity and demand to manage utilization across time while improving transparent communications with stakeholders.

Another approach is a variation of creating a workflow from Lean Principles where people become cross-functional or multi-skilled, working across boundaries while ensuring consistent service delivery. Demand is predictable and manageable; this strategy improves communication between resource managers and stakeholders. There are several ways to optimize in this area, each with unique primary and secondary values to be realized. In the end, the goal is to find and maintain a balance that improves efficiency without overutilizing people to the point that it creates risk, impacts their performance or causes them to burn out. Mike Jones, SVP Facility Operations at Salute Mission Critical, commented, "We brought a new model to the industry with multi-skilled operators and broke down the barrier between the various silos that had encumbered efficient operations on site. Combining all onsite functions under one organization reduces the number of people required onsite and increases staff resiliency due to optimal training and procedures. This Lean Principles method reduces commuting waste and optimizes the number of people associated with each project. The industry has embraced this new model and is driving bottom line savings and resolving the personnel shortage problem."

Optimizing raw materials has a broader scope than most initially understand but is key to sustainability as it becomes a component of a culture focused on reducing resource consumption. Highly integrated systems and processes will drive sustainability by leveraging the right mix of data center measurements standards based on the business requirements. Key areas include:

- Powering a data center - reducing electrical power generation from fossil fuels by way of geothermal, wind and solar energy sources
- Reducing water consumption - especially significant when understanding the local water supply - verifying if there is enough water to meet the water and energy demands (Consider what could happen to the business if a local government cuts off the water

supply to a data center to prioritize offering water to its citizens)
- Sustainable building materials and construction processes – eco-friendly building materials produce lower carbon emissions during production and use
- Strict waste management - 70% of all toxic waste in the US is created by data centers every year.[3] Not throwing away decommissioned equipment, using certified recycling and leveraging sustainable goods personal protective equipment (PPE) is a great start to being good stewards with resources
- Disciplined equipment management – ensuring that all equipment (IT & facilities) are employed in the most optimal manner or removed from the environment
- Predictive maintenance plans with a focus on thresholds, risk mitigation, and optimization of contractors

Step 3: Sustainability Road Map, Measurements & Goal Setting

Sustainability Road Maps (SRM) provide a competitive advantage in business resilience, market opportunity, employee satisfaction, customer acquisition, retention and investor values. A strategic plan of execution will provide:

- A program purpose and business case for stakeholders to show the intersection of sustainability and business growth
- Insight into financial and material risks and opportunities that may arise
- A baseline and scenario analysis to break down enterprise risk management
- Metrics for reporting that will measure how the program is progressing with a goal of achieving Net-Zero within a certain time frame

- Capital expenditure and investment calculations to better analyze environmental and social impacts by using ESG ratings
- Transparency through communications in the industry and with customers to demonstrate actions have been taken toward program commitments

Having goals associated with the road map can help facilities improve upon future sustainability implementation. As the industry learns more about different practices to become more sustainable, the goals can be adjusted to transform services and solutions.

Peter Drucker once said, "(only) what gets measured, gets managed". Reasonable sustainability goals have targets across all the areas of the organization. As you establish the key metrics it is important to realize that the value is not in a single data point but being able to trend the data over time and use the results to determine progress.

As with most programs, the first step is to baseline the current situation with comprehensive data to do two things; develop goals that will drive change and make informed decisions that will have a positive improvement. The UN has 17 sustainable development goals (SDGs). They are big and revolutionary in nature, not just incremental changes. We've all seen companies announce big sustainability goals like "carbon neutral by 2030" or "reduce emissions by 50%". These are the types of goals that require fundamental and innovative changes to business models. In goal setting, it's also important that we have incremental steps and targets that are achievable but also measurable.

It is important to map out the inputs and outputs that contribute to your organization's baseline, as we need to know where opportunities exist and how resources should be allocated to making the change. Once you have the tools and processes to manage the data, it will be easier to measure the impact of your organization's work to meet the goals.

Although there are over 130 discrete and measurable aspects

to the road map to implement, you can start with the top 5 most common metrics as a baseline but remember to use them in context of desired outcomes within an operational scheme to avoid the pitfalls of reporting:

- Data Center Infrastructure Efficiency (DCIE)
- Power Usage Effectiveness (PUE)
- Carbon Usage Effectiveness (CUE)
- Water Usage Effectiveness (WUE)
- Electronics Disposal Efficiency (EDE)

The key to effectively managing the life cycle of the data center is to align industry standards and metrics with customer stakeholders and implement the Key Performance Indicators (KPI) that most effectively reflect performance against sustainability objectives. The wealth of standards and metrics that have been identified must be integrated into an operational scheme that drives performance and continuous improvement. Standards and metrics are driven by behaviors and implementing the appropriate systems and processes will drive results that can be measured and managed while serving as the basis for future planning and continuous improvement.

With KPIs established, the next step is to implement an effective real-time monitoring solution that can immediately identify deviations and support key functions in the change management process. Change management procedures must be in place to capture key metrics before and after the action to ensure that expected outcomes are achieved and importantly that action have delivered the intended positive impact to the environment. Ideally, the change management procedures and monitoring solution will enable simulations to quantify opportunities and aid in developing a structured implementation plan. Given the rapidly changing nature of data centers, effective monitoring solutions are critical.

Step 4: Methodical Audits

Whether you are an operations service provider or an internal operations group, it is critical to establish a disciplined external and internal audit and certification program to ensure transparency and accountability. Strategic audits with supporting operational audits will assure sustainability in a rapidly changing environment. As the industry matures, procurement specialists will begin to include these requirements in requests for proposals (RFP) to operations service providers. With that, boards of directors will begin to enforce these standards universally. Self-certifying is only useful if done as a prep task for an external certification. Without external auditing, the scrutiny required to ensure compliance will fall short of the desired outcome.

Key strategic audit programs include:

ESG

- From a sustainability point of view, this is a critical audit to be conducted and sustained. It includes the analysis of external and internal factors affecting the organizations sustainability. These factors include areas such as climate change legislation, energy use and recycling rates.
- The goal is to continuously be driving to the highest possible sustainability profile and to meet stakeholders' expectations through transparency and accountability.

Social Responsibility

- This audit will include key areas such as culture, corporate social responsibility (CSR) strategy, contracts with suppliers and regulatory filings to ensure the emphasis of CSR is evident at the policy and practice level.
- This audit is more complex than it may appear as it

will also review any negative impacts of CSR on the bottom line and supplier relationships, including human rights records for suppliers.

International Organization for Standardization (ISO)

Any operations organization must evolve and embrace international standards to ensure customer expectations are met. While every organization is different, the key ISO standards and compliance areas that data center operators must achieve are listed below. Each has a wealth of information publicly available for those new to this area. Still, the key is the same with any process. Operators should embrace these standards holistically and not just implement them to satisfy marketing requirements as it will have unintended consequences.

- ISO 9001 – Quality Management
- ISO 27001 – Information Security Management
- ISO 37001 – Anti-Bribery Management
- ISO 14001 – Environmental Management
- ISO 45001 – Occupational Health and Safety

Effective monitoring will provide real time analytics to help you efficiently manage the data center. Audits are a complimentary function to help ensure a disciplined review of key data, processes and best practices. Audits help identify the main impacts of a facility and compare different technologies, supply chain opportunities, best practices and continuous process improvement. Analysis activities support areas such as:

- Determining when to retire equipment versus re-deploy it
- Identifying opportunities for using AI
- Consolidating less efficient systems to reduce overall energy use and improve system utilization.

Kristen Vosmaer, President at Salute Mission Critical, commented, "As an operations service provider we integrate into our client's sustainability framework, so it was important to us to obtain an ESG rating. Combining ESG with our ISO certifications, corporate social responsibility programs and best practices with operational audits allows us to continuously improve, fosters transparency and drives bottom line results for clients."

Important Operational Audits include:

IT Asset Disposition (ITAD) Audit

- Identifying what infrastructure and IT hardware can be reduced, replaced, or optimized, including virtualizing of processing and storage. Those that are underutilized or perform infrequent processing or work that can be scheduled are good candidates for virtualization. Hardware that is past its useful life for production purposes may be a good candidate for a pilot or sandbox development architecture.
- Implementing ongoing change management procedures that continuously consider the efficient removal of equipment that is rendered redundant by the new technologies being deployed will eliminate the need for large "true up" type projects in the future.

Design and Planning Review

- Reviewing the difference between building a data center with wood versus concrete. Consider sustainability, cost, construction schedule, material strength requirements, building codes, and operational controls such as temperature and humidity.
- Assessing cooling strategies based on local ambient conditions and available solutions based on your specific requirements. Cooling solutions range from the chip up through the rack to the data center and the

best balance may be a hybrid solution given multiple applications needs.

- Regional or metro spare parts management versus local on-site strategies to reduce manufacturing and storage demands for infrequently and often higher value parts that are available to meet service levels for replacement but essentially shared with other locations until used and stock is replenished.
- Ensuring sustainable supply chain and building materials planning, such as green concrete, smart glass, etc. will drive further positive results.

Full Emissions Audit

- Verifying emissions associated with the purchase of all equipment to ensure EHS regulatory compliance in the areas of permitting, reporting, health and safety risk management, and spill prevention, containment and countermeasure (SPCC) planning.

Scope 2 + 3 Greenhouse Gas (GHG) Emissions Audit

- Verifying emissions associated with the purchase of purchased electricity, heat, steam, goods, business travel, commuting, waste disposal, transportation, distribution, investments and assets

Institutionalizing audits is most effectively accomplished by including them in the annual plans so that they can be budgeted and planned. An overall annual calendar of key events should include key operational processes such as audits, training, drills and change reviews as well as business support functions such as budget input and HR reviews.

Step 5: Local Requirements

A data center is subject to local regulations and requirements and these change over time. That may be blatantly obvious, but it is important to understand and incorporate local requirements in your plans. Key areas to consider are:

- Evaluate local requirements that influence maintenance plans. For instance, a noise reduction standard can affect timing and occurrence of maintenance cycles.
- Many countries have sustainability training/guidelines that should be incorporated.
- Governments may offer tax incentives for sustainable practices.
- Utility providers often provide grants and rebates for energy efficiency projects.
- Collaborate and understand what other building operators are adopting and share best practices.

The brevity of this step is due to the large variability of each location and should not imply it is not significant both in effort and impact. Working closely with local authorities and planning councils will ensure thoughtful planning and drive positive outcomes.

Our Duty to Making a Sustainable Ethical Impact that Drives Bottom Line Results

If you do it right, sustainable operations can drive bottom-line results that will have long-term social, environmental and economic benefits. Embrace the challenge and unleash an empowered workforce with sustainability as an integrated part of every function. Your operations teams are the key to sustainability. As leaders in this industry, we must drive the change and make the difference for generations to come.

1. Patrizio, Andy. 2019. "Data Center Operators Not Keen On Green: Survey." Network World. December 17, 2019. https://www.networkworld.com/article/3490331/data-center-operators-not-keen-on-green-survey.html.
2. Vosmaer, Kristen and Lee Kirby. 2021. "Data Center Sustainability: Achieving a Carbon Neutral Environment through Data Center Operations." Salute Mission Critical. November 3, 2021. https://salutemissioncritical.com/data-center-sustainability/.
3. Patrizio, Andy. 2019. "Poor Data-center Configuration Leads to Severe Waste Problem." Network World. January 4, 2019. https://www.networkworld.com/article/3330650/poor-data-center-configuration-leads-to-severe-waste-problem.html.

About the Author

LEE KIRBY

Lee has more than 40 years of experience in all aspects of information systems, strategic business development, finance, planning, human resources and administration both in the private and public sectors. Lee has successfully led several technology startups and turn-arounds as well as built and run world-class global operations.

He is a trusted advisor and independent consultant for various organizations in the data center sector and provides interim leadership to emerging and transforming technology companies. His core technical competency focuses on improving the performance of critical infrastructure through sustainable solutions that reduce operating costs across all industries. Lee provides leadership from business strategy development through funding to execution and his focus on sustainable operations has repeatedly driven value to all stakeholders. His primary focus, Salute, launched in 2013 and is focused on providing military veterans with job opportunities. By immersing the veterans and helping them gain experience and skills this initiative delivers a feeder system to the data center industry and the first step in a career for the veterans.

In addition to an MBA from University of Washington and further studies at Henley School of Business in London and Stanford University, Lee holds professional certifications in management and security (ITIL v3 Expert, Lean Six Sigma, CCO). He also serves as a frequent contributor for many industry conferences and publications. In addition to his many years as a successful technology industry leader, he has masterfully balanced a successful military career over 36 years (Ret. Colonel) and continues to serve as an advisor to many veteran support organizations.

EIGHT

Bill Kleyman

POWERING THE FOURTH INDUSTRIAL REVOLUTION: LEVERAGING HUMAN INGENUITY AND INDUSTRY CREATIVITY

Introduction

I'm so happy that you're spending a few minutes with me. I promise we're about to dive into a fascinating conversation around power, humanity, and how we're going to power the most critical pieces of infrastructure that support everything we do today and will do in the future.

This is going to be a somewhat deep dive into the Fourth Industrial Revolution, what's powering our everyday tools, and just how creative we've become to ensure that we design power for a greener tomorrow.

But before we dive in, and since the editors gave me a little bit of white space to get started, I wanted to take you on a journey. We'll take a little trip into how I got started in the technology, communication, and data center industry, and I promise it'll all tie back together. For now, sit back, and enjoy the ride.

Hello from the USSR

I bet you didn't expect that heading. As a millennial, I became a digital native through the tools I use every day to stay connected. However, I'm lucky enough to remember dial-up modems, unbreakable Nokia phones, and the absolute excitement when I got my very first cable modem and a whopping 1.5 Mb/s Internet connection.

But our story goes a little bit further back. I came to the USA in the 90s as a political asylum refugee, and we were fleeing the now-former USSR. I was born in Kyiv, Ukraine and still vividly recall my life as a young person in the Soviet Union. Although I don't have enough time to talk about Chernobyl, the collapse of the USSR, and how we became refugees, I can tell you a fascinating side story that was the nexus of my career in this industry.

From our cozy apartment in Kyiv, my older brother would spend quite a bit of time with me. Our parents worked a lot, so he became the de-facto babysitter. While my brother was in school, he participated in an exciting communications competition. What tool did he use? The telegraph. My brother, Alex, had all the tools, the headphones, the telegraph switch, and the expertise to be one of the best in the USSR. I would watch him while he competed, rapidly moving his fingers to send messages to others all over the country. My favorite moments were when he would let me sit on his lap and try Morse code for myself. He taught me the alphabet, the numerical symbols, and how to communicate essential messages quickly. It's hard to describe the sheer fascination and excitement when I would send a message as a young child. And someone would always reply. Even today, I still remember this as a core memory. I heard the beeps and sounds of an incoming transmission and worked with my brother to feverishly write down what the other person was saying. It was so much fun. It was also the start of my fascination with communication and bringing people closer together with technology.

Hello from the USA

Did it take some time to become acclimated to American culture? You bet it did. But my childhood naïveté and boundless curiosity never waned. To this day, I tell the students that I mentor to never lose their childhood sense of wonder. In high school I took computer and computer science courses, and in college, I studied network engineering and communications. After my initial degree, I continued to study telecommunications earning a Master of Business Administration (MBA) and a Master of Information Systems Management (MISM) in security and data management, and how all of this impacts what we do daily.

From then on, I've never left the technology industry. I've had the chance to work with end users and organizations of all sorts, advanced virtualization systems, cloud design, DevOps, and hyperscale data center ecosystems. Today, I work with a leader in the industry, Switch Data Centers. By partnering with this organization, I get the chance to see just how connected we are as a society and how dependent we are on critical infrastructure.

I've also learned that data runs the planet. And it's at this point that we take a pause. Here's something the leader of my company, Rob Roy, would say: **just because data runs the planet doesn't mean it should ruin it.** Humanity is at a critical point in evolution. We've seen extraordinary advancements with automation, manufacturing, and new technology. We're also seeing how all of this impacts our planet. Today, we're all a part of the Fourth Industrial Revolution.

Let's explore what that means.

Blurring the Lines Between Physical, Digital, and Biological

Data centers are really cool. The modern digital infrastructure is a complex system supporting everything we do today. That smartwatch you're wearing? You guessed it; the data flows through a data center. Did you ask your smart speaker about the weather? That's going through a data center as well. If you're listening to this book via digital audio ten years from now in your vehicle, your smart car is also communicating with a data center.

Every connected activity you participate in has a data center at its core. Now, some of those facilities are larger, and some are smaller. There are also all sorts of mini-definitions for those types of infrastructure, including edge, mist, and even fog computing. Whichever way you decide to define it, you are still leveraging some infrastructure to deliver critical resources.

Here's the crazy part. The pace of our evolution and the speed of the current breakthroughs that we're all experiencing has no historical precedent. This Fourth Industrial Revolution—that we're all a part—of is evolving exponentially rather than at a linear pace.

According to the World Economic Forum:

> The possibilities of billions of people connected by mobile devices, with unprecedented processing power, storage capacity, and access to knowledge, are unlimited. And these possibilities will be multiplied by emerging technology breakthroughs in fields such as artificial intelligence, robotics, the Internet of Things, autonomous vehicles, 3-D printing, nanotechnology, biotechnology, materials science, energy storage, and quantum computing.[1]

If you take a closer look at the world today, you'll see that many of these technologies are already in the mainstream. AI-powered vehicles, smarter airplanes, connected homes, personalized healthcare, synthetic biology, and even quantum computing breakthroughs are all a part of today's life.

However, as I mentioned earlier, data is at the core of it all. And the epicenter of data processing is data centers. So we know that *today* we are a part of the Fourth Industrial Revolution. However, when looking at our impact on this planet, we aren't only trying to be carbon neutral as part of this revolution; unlike previous revolutions, we must design and leverage the Fourth Industrial Revolution to be sustainable and *counteract* the effects of the last three revolutions. And so we reach the all-important thesis of this little chapter: *Powering the Fourth Industrial Revolution.*

Remember, data runs the planet. But it certainly shouldn't ruin it. This is where it gets interesting. How do we power the Fourth Industrial Revolution to ensure a more sustainable future? And how do we ensure that we begin to reduce greenhouse gas emissions measurably? We as an industry must continue to do what we're so good at: **innovate**.

Powering the Future Will Require Innovation and Creativity

A recent Wall Street Journal article noted that to meet global energy demand and climate aspirations, investments in clean energy would need to grow from around $1.1 trillion this year to $3.4 trillion a year until 2030.[2] The investment would advance technology, transmission, and storage, among other things.

Here's another significant point to understand: going green isn't only good for the environment, it's also great for your business. Executives now realize that investing in sustainable organizations is also excellent for the bottom line. A recent post from Data Center Frontier notes that investors will be part of the green energy revolution as they seek to align their portfolios with climate resilience. There will be more green funding deals in the future, driven by investors' growing appetite for sustainable options. According to Morningstar, 76 new climate-aware funds were launched globally in 2020, which now tracks more than 400 mutual funds and exchange-traded funds globally that have climate change as a critical theme.[3]

"Sustainable debt is likely to go through the roof this year," said Dr. Richard Mattison, the CEO of Trucost, a unit of S&P that assesses corporate risk from climate change. "This year, we expect to see many more funds springing up targeted at sustainability and green outcomes. Where investors want to put their money is going to lead to a huge change in capital markets, and most financial institutions recognize that."[4]

Before we dive into some creative solutions to power the

future, it's important to note that green solutions are already gaining market share in the energy sector. We hit a pretty significant milestone in 2019. That year, before the onset of the pandemic, the United States consumed more renewable energy than coal for the first time since 1885.[5]

So, is this goodbye to using fossil fuels? Almost "We're starting the long, long goodbye," states Bob Fryklund, a strategist at IHS Markit.[6]

Driving this "long goodbye" are amazingly innovative solutions to power some of the world's largest and most advanced technology platforms. Remember how I mentioned that we would need to be creative to power the future? Well, let's take a look at some innovative ways we'll be able to power our future digital requirements.

- **Dominion Energy's Coastal Virginia Offshore Wind Project.** First, it's important to note that offshore wind projects are actively gaining momentum as of this writing. However, there's one fascinating project to document. In July 2021 Dominion Energy announced an extraordinary project. The proposed 2.6-gigawatt Coastal Virginia Offshore Wind (CVOW) commercial project will be the largest planned offshore wind farm in the United States. "I'm thrilled to see this project underway as it's an exciting step toward a clean energy economy that creates good jobs in the Commonwealth," said US Senator Tim Kaine (D-VA). "I will keep pushing for clean energy investments in Virginia to boost our economy and build a more sustainable future."[7]
- **Switch's Water Improvement Pipeline Project.** We can't forget about water and water scarcity as a consideration for a greener tomorrow. Nevada Governor Steve Sisolak joined leaders from every local government in the Truckee River region to celebrate the commencement of the construction of the

Regional Water Improvement Pipeline Project. Switch is leading the development of a 16-mile, 4,000 acre-foot effluent water pipeline in Northern Nevada to support meaningful water conservation efforts.[8] Consider this: today, Switch operates a 1.3 million square foot data center at the Citadel Campus. The company intends to build up to 7.2 million square feet of IT capacity and a total power capacity of 650 megawatts. The exceptional part here is that this pipeline will support *all water requirements at the multi-million square-foot campus.* Water conservation efforts done by data center leaders are especially critical. For example, this project will reduce nitrates that would otherwise flow into the Truckee River. It will also help protect local wildlife and endangered species. Remember, critical infrastructure isn't only trying to reverse the impacts of the previous three revolutions; it's also working hard to be good stewards of the community and good neighbors to surrounding areas.

- **Japan: The World Leader in Floating Solar Panels.** A recent post from the World Economic Forum puts it best: how do you increase your solar energy output when you need all your land for agriculture and housing? Take to the water. The world's first floating solar plant was built in Japan, in Aichi Prefecture in central Honshu. The country's many inland lakes and reservoirs are now home to 73 of the world's 100 largest floating solar plants and account for half of those plants' 246 megawatts of solar capacity. The biggest Japanese floating solar plant sits behind the Yamakura Dam at Ichihara in Chiba Prefecture. It covers 18 hectares, can power nearly 5,000 homes, and saves more than 8,000 tonnes of carbon dioxide a year.[9]

- **The Power of the Tidal Turbine.** Using the power of tidal currents is such a remarkable innovation. A tidal turbine weighing 680 metric tons and dubbed "the world's most powerful" has started grid-connected power generation at the European Marine Energy Centre in Orkney, an archipelago located north of mainland Scotland. In a recent announcement, Scottish engineering firm Orbital Marine Power explained how its 2-megawatt oxygen turbine had been anchored in a body of water called the Fall of Warness, with a subsea cable linking it to a local electricity network on land. It's expected that the turbine, which is 74 meters long, will "operate in the waters off Orkney for the next 15 years," the company said, and have "the capacity to meet the annual electricity demand of around 2,000 UK homes."[10]

- **Switch Gigawatt 1:** Recently, Switch announced Rob Roy's Gigawatt Nevada, a massive solar energy and battery storage project. This development is one of the technology industry's most significant solar footprint and battery storage projects. Upon completion, it will reach one Gigawatt of solar power across Nevada and over 800 MW hours of battery storage leveraging Tesla Megapack technologies. "In the midst of this unprecedented moment in our state's history, Switch and its partners are investing $1.3 billion, creating over a thousand new jobs and accelerating Nevada's leadership in the world's renewable energy economy," said Nevada Governor Steve Sisolak. Additionally, Switch has dedicated local, renewable resources for solar power, Switch Station 1 and Switch Station 2, located in Southern Nevada, generating 179MW of green energy.[11]

- **Nuclear-Powered Data Centers.** Want another extraordinary example? Imagine a nuclear reactor powers your future data center. A recent DataCenterDynamics post discussed how small modular reactors (SMRs) are under development by the Rolls-Royce consortium.[12] And, if you think this is a far-fetched notion, it's not. At the 2022 AFCOM Data Center World Conference,[13] the Department of Energy and other presenters will discuss deploying and financing SMRs in the data center industry. They're also doing a complete virtual reality walkthrough of an actual SMR.

Pretty exciting stuff, right? Now, let's shift for a moment and focus on selecting the right partners to ensure a sustainable future. To do so, we need to discuss greenhouse gas emissions briefly.

Eliminating GHG to Support a Greener Tomorrow

The EPA states that carbon emissions are responsible for more than 80% of overall greenhouse gas (GHG) emissions. To remain sustainable, enterprises must monitor and report their carbon emissions, which is the crucial first step in reducing them. To help define a company's carbon footprint, greenhouse gas emissions are generally categorized into three groups, or scopes, under the Greenhouse Gas (GHG) Protocol. There are three scopes to consider.

- Scope 1. This measure covers direct emissions from owned or controlled sources.
- Scope 2. This measure covers indirect emissions from the generation of purchased electricity, steam, heating, and cooling the reporting company consumes.
- Scope 3. This measure includes all other indirect emissions in a company's value chain.

To power a more sustainable future, it's essential to challenge your partners around their emissions strategy and ensure that it's not just a long-term goal. For example, data center leaders like Switch have already achieved ZERO Scope 1 and Scope 2 carbon emissions.

Again, as part of your journey towards powering the Fourth Industrial Revolution, be sure to look for partners actively tracking towards net zero.

Hello from the Future

Thanks for making it this far along. If you're reading this from the not-so-distant future, let me know how your nuclear-powered data center is running. Or, maybe you can find me and update me on your excellent new storage and solar project leveraging the latest sustainable battery technology.

We're making tremendous strides in creating sustainable solutions to power some of the most critical pieces of infrastructure. However, it won't be one company or one technology that will solve our challenges.

I was introduced to communications through a telegraph. Today, I work with the backbone of the internet and get the chance to see just how vast our connected society has become. The most significant difference between when I started in this industry versus today is my understanding of the systems that power it all. Working at Switch has allowed me to see what private industry can do, and it also gives me hope that our future will be brighter and greener.

So, hello from the future. I hope that whoever is reading this can look back reflectively and think, "My goodness, how far we've come!" It's up to all of us to become champions of this planet and ensure that we build a more sustainable Fourth Industrial Revolution.

1. Schwab, Klaus. 2016. "The Fourth Industrial Revolution: What It Means and How to Respond." World Economic Forum. January 14, 2016. https://www.weforum.org/agenda/2016/01/the-fourth-industrial-revolution-what-it-means-and-how-to-respond/.
2. Christopher M. Matthews, Collin Eaton, and Benoit Faucon. 2021. "Behind the Energy Crisis: Fossil Fuel Investment Drops, and Renewables Aren't Ready." Wall Street Journal, October 17, 2021. https://www.wsj.com/articles/energy-crisis-fossil-fuel-investment-renewables-gas-oil-prices-coal-wind-solar-hydro-power-grid-11634497531.

3. Miller, Rich. 2021. "Sustainable Finance: The Next Frontier in Data Centers' Climate Response." Data Center Frontier. April 22, 2021. https://datacenterfrontier.com/sustainable-finance-the-next-frontier-in-data-centers-climate-response/.
4. Ibid.
5. Blunt, Katherine. 2020. "U.S. Consumed More Renewables than Coal for First Time in 134 Years." Wall Street Journal. May 28, 2020. https://www.wsj.com/articles/u-s-consumed-more-renewables-than-coal-for-first-time-in-134-years-11590691919.
6. Christopher M. Matthews, Collin Eaton, and Benoit Faucon. 2021.
7. Dominion Energy. 2021. "Dominion Energy's Coastal Virginia Offshore Wind Project Achieves Key Regulatory Milestone; Consistent with Project Timeline." Dominion Energy MediaRoom, July 1, 2021. https://news.dominionenergy.com/2021-07-01-Dominion-Energys-Coastal-Virginia-Offshore-Wind-Project-Achieves-Key-Regulatory-Milestone-Consistent-with-Project-Timeline.
8. Miller, Rich. 2021b. "Switch Will Support Reno Data Center Campus with Reclaimed Water." Data Center Frontier. October 27, 2021. https://datacenterfrontier.com/switch-will-support-reno-data-center-campus-with-reclaimed-water/.
9. Broom, Douglas. 2019. "How Japan Became the World Leader in Floating Solar Power." World Economic Forum. March 22, 2019. https://www.weforum.org/agenda/2019/03/japan-is-the-world-leader-in-floating-solar-power/.
10. Frangoul, Anmar. 2021. "The 'world's Most Powerful Tidal Turbine' Starts to Export Power to the Grid." CNBC. July 28, 2021. https://www.cnbc.com/2021/07/28/worlds-most-powerful-tidal-turbine-starts-to-export-power-to-grid-.html.
11. Energy Industry Review. 2020. "Gigawatt 1, World's 'Largest behind-the-Meter Solar Project.'" Energy Industry Review. July 27, 2020. https://energyindustryreview.com/renewables/gigawatt-1-worlds-largest-behind-the-meter-solar-project/.
12. Judge, Peter. 2021. "Rolls-Royce Said to Be Pitching Small Nuclear Reactors to Power Data Centers." Data Center Dynamics. October 5, 2021. https://www.datacenterdynamics.com/en/news/rolls-royce-said-to-be-pitching-small-nuclear-reactors-to-power-data-centers/.
13. Bill Bubenicek and Kugelmass, "Deploying and Financing SMRs for the Data Center Sector." Workshop, Data Center World 2022, Austin, TX. March 28, 2022.

About the Author

BILL KLEYMAN

Bill Kleyman is the EVP of Digital Solutions at Switch, a global data center, and sustainability industry leader. Ranked globally by an Onalytica Study as one of the leaders in cloud computing and data security, Bill Kleyman is an award-winning technologist. He has spent more than 15 years specializing in the cybersecurity, cloud, and data center industry. His most recent efforts with the Infrastructure Masons were recognized when he received the 2020 IM100 Award and the 2021 iMasons Education Champion Award for his work with numerous HBCUs and for helping diversify the digital infrastructure talent pool.

Bill works with Switch's marketing, branding, engagement, and technology teams to support new business initiatives, marketing programs, and industry messaging. As an industry analyst, speaker, and blogger, Bill helps the Switch team develop new ways to impact the digital infrastructure industry as leaders in sustainability, Exascale design, ESG, power development, and more.

You can read more of Bill's contributions as a contributing editor in Data Center Knowledge, Data Center Frontier, InformationWeek, and others.

NINE

Bruce Lehrman

LEADING FROM WITHIN HOLDS THE KEY TO A MORE SUSTAINABLE FUTURE

In his 1994 book, *The Pale Blue Dot,* famed NASA astronomer Carl Sagan writes a passage discussing a moment at the end of Voyager 1's mission. Before the spacecraft left our solar system, it turned back to photograph one last image of Earth, by then only appearing as a barely recognizable pixel. In his book, Sagan elaborates on what it means to see a vision of the earth as minuscule and insignificant: "our posturings, our imagined self-importance, the delusion that we have some privileged position in the universe, are challenged by this point of pale light. Our planet is a lonely speck in the great enveloping cosmic dark. In our obscurity, in all this vastness, there is no hint that help will come from elsewhere to save us from ourselves". [1]

One phrase from that passage sticks out to me—*there is no hint that help will come from elsewhere*. In my years of data center industry leadership, I've explored green initiatives and conservatorship. In my early career, I thought I could look elsewhere for help, guidance, and structure in pursuing a greener data center. My views, however, have progressed through my journey. I now know that it was always up to us, as individuals in the industry, to take leadership of these measures. The solution couldn't come from anyone but those who lived the challenges first-hand and were willing to think differently in pursuit of something better. I would like to take the opportunity to share some successes, some failures, and how I believe we can take hold of a greener future for the data center industry.

A Look Back

The tech industry in the mid-1990s was fast-paced and exciting, with infinite unknown possibilities. That's where I earned my stripes as an entrepreneur—including some involvement in the world's first internet data center in Palo Alto. I entered the data center industry as co-founder and CEO of Involta in 2007. We began by renovating an abandoned telecommunications data center outside of my hometown of Cedar Rapids, Iowa. We prioritized conservation from the very start.

When creating the Involta logo, we chose a design with four blue blocks to symbolize integrity, innovation, confidence, and stability. At the center is a green block that represents energy efficiency. We wanted green initiatives to be at the figurative—and literal—core of our organization, and we differentiated Involta by focusing on how to be as efficient and green as we could as an operator. Implementing this approach into our developmental strategy practice, however, proved to be complex.

Around this time, LEED-certified buildings were emerging on the scene as the premier construction standard for businesses committed to energy conservation. Our corporate mindset was that we wanted to be at the forefront of eco-friendly measures, so we eagerly pursued LEED's standards for building our new data center facility. Unfortunately, we found the LEED system to be woefully inadequate. What we discovered was that LEED certification would apply only to our office area, excluding the entire data center from the calculations. While we did achieve LEED-certified status, it made little sense from an energy efficiency standpoint. We received specific guidance toward aspects like our parking lot and staff lunchroom; however, the program failed to address the hardware and infrastructure of our 10,000 square foot colocation facility. Accomplishing the top standard available fell far short, and I felt disenchanted.

The disappointment stemmed from the overwhelming sense of the opportunity and responsibility I felt to connect my personal conservation and sustainability beliefs with my professional duties. Away from work, I'm committed to environmental responsibility. My perspective is that we all have a personal responsibility to do what we can in our own way. We can't change everything immediately, but we can all think about what we can do to improve incrementally. In aggregate, it all matters. For instance, in an effort to live as efficiently as possible, I've installed solar panels on two homes and drive an electric car. I believe it's not enough for me to apply green principles in my personal life. As an investor, entrepreneur, and business owner, I have sway over a greater number of variables and a greater sphere of influence in which to make positive choices for the environment than the average person.

After all, a data center is not just any business. As an industry, we're consuming three percent of the world's power, 10 to 50 times as much as a typical commercial office building on average —and growing fast.[2] The pure volume of energy used to operate simply isn't much of a consideration for most businesses, but for data centers, it's top of mind. Managing the electricity bill is a discipline that good operators need to develop. Back in 2007 as our team worked to lift our first data center operation off the ground, I was acutely aware of this massive responsibility on my shoulders.

Everything changed in 2009 when I visited a green data center conference with one of my business partners. It was incredibly thought-provoking and opened my eyes to a world of new technologies for gaining improved energy efficiency. I remember learning how Google built their own servers where every component was 12-volt DC power. I was familiar with the typical power supply for a computer with different components running on different voltages. Some components would run on 12-volt, some on four-volt, and some on six-volt. Power supplies are needed to convert the AC power to DC in order to produce all the different voltages, which is inefficient. Google, I learned, was planning to solve that inefficiency with custom, extra-efficient servers in their data centers, with batteries built directly into them.

I also learned about exciting new cooling strategies for areas with unusually high power costs. In Japan, where there are different costs for power in the daytime compared to nighttime, data centers would freeze water at night to use as a coolant during the day to optimize timing and take advantage of the better rates.

The conference was revelatory. I realized that there was no roadmap to reduce carbon emissions. The way to reach a greener data center was not to follow an across-the-board set of recommendations like LEED. Instead, the solution for data centers like ours was to make incremental, everyday improvements focused on a commitment to energy efficiency. There was never going to be a wholesale answer. Each data center needs to take leadership and work through each aspect of their operation to find places where they can make good, conscious business decisions toward a goal of zero emissions. Using this foundation, we wanted to guide Involta's developmental strategy toward environmental health initiatives. The next challenge was learning how to implement this approach into practice within a dynamic organization.

Individuals Go Far, Teams Go Farther

Driving innovation is a team sport. Although I believe strongly in pursuing green initiatives, I am part of a larger whole with many different viewpoints. At Involta, we've created advisory boards for three different sectors we serve, and our own board and investors continually challenge us to drive innovation and efficiency. To make a difference, you need to get funds approved, and you need buy-in from every level of an organization. Moving the inner workings of a company toward energy efficiency requires discussion and, often, some persuasion and compromise. Along the way,

I've learned three important lessons in working together to implement new, greener policies and procedures.

First, we have to balance innovation with reliability at all times. We want to make sustainability our priority while also acknowledging that uptime is essential. The goal is to stay as current as possible, but that doesn't mean trying any new gadget that comes along. Our customers are hospitals and banks that need their systems running 100% of the time. We can't take chances on cutting-edge technology—we have to know with certainty. At Involta, we say our approach is *leading edge*, but not *bleeding edge*.

Second, it's important to try to recognize the difference between being busy and achieving results. When aiming for green improvements, it can be easy to fall into the trap of holding meetings, making plans, and feeling like you're moving in the right direction. Yet, after a period of time, you look back and see that you're not truly reaching the kind of goals you were setting out to achieve. Beyond good intentions, there needs to be a strong planning process and a sound measurement system. Green initiatives should be quantified and time-bound so you know what success looks like and each person's aim is well-defined. We inserted conservation goals into our larger review system, checking how we're making progress and ensuring optimization regularly. Power usage effectiveness ratio (PUE) is a key metric we use to track trends regarding the effectiveness of our green initiative projects. Small adjustments can have a significant impact on energy consumption, and monitoring PUE provides quantitative results.

Third, when it comes to environmental measures that require capital investments, we still need to evaluate decisions in light of a return on investment (ROI). Making decisions toward conservation still requires crunching the numbers. On the one hand, we are not in the position to, say, spend $100 million on a solar farm to move our data centers to fully renewable energy. On the other hand, data centers don't have to go bankrupt to make significant emissions reductions. I've learned to work with our team to set an ROI threshold on energy efficiency projects, and we work through the economics together. The good news is that going greener means saving energy, and there should almost always be some payback. In this view, the decision is primarily only a matter of *how long* the move to greener technology will take to create cost savings, not a matter of *if* it will. Each initiative is distinct, but we can differentiate the projects into categories: short-term payback, long-term payback, and no immediate payback.

As a case in point, some green initiatives provided an immediate and considerable payback, such as addressing efficient and precise air supply distribution. Our aim was to provide consistent air supply to computer room IT equipment to increase overall data center efficiencies. We worked with a company called Ductsox to design a custom solution for providing cool air to our cold aisle in a type of fabric sleeve as opposed to metal. The result is the ability to turn nozzles on to create more air in the places that really need it. The partnership was an immediate success, and we implemented the custom pieces across all our facilities with impressive results. Ductsox went on to standardize a modified version of the solution and now markets them industry-wide as Datasox.

Ductsox Design

Other initiatives produced results that took longer to come to fruition. Although the implementation of free cooling solutions to reduce the electrical consumption required for mechanical cooling is now widely implemented in the industry, Involta was an early adopter. More than 10 years ago, we made the decision to transition our facilities to a solution that takes advantage of cooler outside air to minimize the need for mechanical cooling. By installing new Computer Room Air Conditioning (CRAC) units with economizer pumps, outside air is automatically used when the air temperature reaches a certain level. When we put the numbers together, the ability to drive better overall PUE figures made economic sense, but the payback period was much longer than most of our other projects. Pursuing different initiatives could have delivered faster results, but we decided that free cooling was the right thing to do for the long haul.

Another example of an initiative we prioritized even with a long payback schedule is when we installed hot and cold aisle containment. CRAC unit power consumption is one of the highest power overheads in data center operational expenses, and the containment of cold supply or hot exhaust air drives an ideal temperature delta to achieve the most efficient operations of CRAC units. From a return standpoint, pursuing this initiative has benefits, as it drives down the PUE ratio and results in significant power savings—even though it may not be on the timeline we'd like to see in the marketplace. Committing to spending money on technology to enable longer-term savings can be challenging. However, knowing that these sustainability investments are what enterprises expect from a world-class operationally efficient data center facility will ultimately pay dividends in the end.

Certain projects sometimes fall into the category of delivering neither a long-term nor short-term financial payback, and we typically choose not to chase them. However, that's not always the case—especially when it's the right thing to do. Involta has always been driven to be active in the communities we serve. When a major natural disaster occurred recently near our headquarters in central Iowa, we felt compelled to launch a powerful corporate response. A massive storm known as a *derecho* struck the area, with 140 mile-per-hour winds destroying over 1,000 houses and damaging approximately 90 percent of all other buildings in the area. Involta facilities experienced no downtime, allowing us to help get regional businesses back up and running within hours. We also made workstations, network connectivity, computers, and phone lines available for impacted companies. Besides power lines, buildings, crops, vehicles, and silos, the storm also devastated the surrounding ecosystem. An estimated 65 percent of trees in the area were damaged or destroyed. In response, we decided to participate in a program led by a local non-profit organization to replant and replace native trees in the area. As a result, all Involta employees could receive three trees to plant wherever they chose, sponsored by the company. It was a rare capital outlay with no chance of any payback, but it was something we gladly decided to enact.

Looking Ahead

When Involta was still young, we went out into the marketplace to find power providers that would provide a green energy rate so we could offer the capability to our customers. At the time, not one client was willing to pay the extra two cents per kilowatt-hour for renewable energy. It was shocking and discouraging. There was so little interest that we stopped providing the option. However, over the last 10 to 15 years, there has been a considerable change in the perception of power consumption—to the degree that we are going to reintroduce green energy options. Paying a bit more per kilowatt-hour no longer seems unreasonable.

There are other signs of new leadership in the industry beginning to shift perception, change market conditions, and swing best practices for the better. Large tech companies are now requesting renewable energy, creating more availability, and driving the power costs of that availability down. When Google built its data center in Iowa, its requirement was 100 percent renewable energy sources. In response, the company created a process where the local power supplier—MidAmerican Energy—built major wind generation projects in the area. Microsoft and Facebook are both in Iowa too. When those companies require renewable energy, it drives power companies to meet the demand on an aggressive timeframe. Of course, smaller companies are not in the position to commit to massive amounts of long-term power like the tech giants are, but the point is that when these organizations leverage their position to create the opportunity for alternative power, we all benefit. It's a question of taking leadership.

I can see a similar game-changing trend emerging with investors. Increased attention to environmental, social and governance (ESG) ratings, for instance, are creating a different approach toward the energy source a business utilizes. Funds now exist where investors will only commit to companies with appropriate ESG policies, even when the return on investment may be lower. There are now enough investors whose portfolios are targeting ESG scores that the market is beginning to shift on that basis.

There are a lot of reasons for optimism. One positive aspect concerning unclear outcomes is that they sometimes have a way of becoming more apparent as time passes and technology progresses. As such, we've seen data centers invest in initiatives with questionable payback that became more efficient over time. For instance, investments in solar initiatives represented very little payback 10 years ago, but today are inching ever closer to cost parity. According to the latest survey from the Uptime Institute, the average PUE of a data center stands at 1.58.[3] This figure has been declining steadily since 2007 (when it was 2.5) and 2013 (when it was 1.65).[4] The average PUE for a Google data center is 1.12, but its facility in Oklahoma had a score of just 1.08 during the last three months of 2018.[5] These numbers show excellent progress and the industry's ability to keep an eye on sustainable practices even if the payback is not determined to be viable at one point in time. Innovation can change the landscape, and we need to be on the lookout for actions now that may bear fruit in the future.

Taking the Lead

If I could go back in time to the Bruce of 2007, I would tell him not to wait, not to look around for answers from elsewhere. I would ask him to dig in, get his hands dirty, and find the answers himself. Managers and executives taking individual leadership have propelled the data center industry's green initiatives to where they are today, and that's what we have to bank on into the future.

In many ways, we're still in the industry's wild west period, where anything goes. Power usage continues to climb, and there isn't yet any governance cracking down on energy consumption. The global impacts of continued consumption are catastrophic, so we must act now. Instead of waiting for overarching regulations for each data center's energy use, industry leadership can make proactive changes toward green energy sources and sustainable operations. The time to lead the data center industry to a bright, carbon-neutral future is right now. It's a matter of forging your own path. After all, *help isn't coming from elsewhere to save us from ourselves.*

---

1. Szoldra, Paul. 2016. "26 Years Ago, Carl Sagan Gave Us an Incredible Perspective on Our Planet." Business Insider. February 14, 2016. https://www.businessinsider.com/pale-blue-dot-carl-sagan-2016-1.
2. Office of Energy Efficiency & Renewable Energy. "Data Centers and Servers." Energy.gov. https://www.energy.gov/eere/buildings/data-centers-and-servers.
3. Hall, Christine. 2018. "Uptime's Data Center Survey Shows Increased Downtime and More Efficient Power Use." Data Center Knowledge. November 14, 2018. https://www.datacenterknowledge.com/uptime/uptimes-data-center-survey-shows-increased-downtime-and-more-efficient-power-use.
4. Ibid.
5. Google Data Centers. "Efficiency." https://www.google.com/about/datacenters/efficiency/.

About the Author

BRUCE LEHRMAN

Bruce Lehrman, Chief Executive Officer of Involta, is best known for his entrepreneurial spirit and ability to build world-class technology organizations. He has been involved in three greenfield business start-ups and has also worked with large, nationally recognized brands. In 2007, Bruce founded Involta LLC, a privately held hybrid IT services company headquartered in Cedar Rapids, Iowa. In early 2022, the company was acquired by Carlyle Group, one of the largest and most diversified global investment firms.

Involta was named the second-fastest growing IT Company in the country in 2010, according to Inc. Magazine 500 Fastest Growing Companies (#40 overall) and has remained on the Inc. 500/5000 list since. In 2016, Involta was selected Technology Company of the Year by the Technology Association of Iowa, and Bruce was named CEO of the Year at the same event. He has also been recognized as the Entrepreneur of the Year by the Cedar Rapids Chamber of Commerce and as a finalist for the Entrepreneur of the Year by Ernst & Young.

Bruce sits on the Board of the Entrepreneurial Development Center, Technology Association of Iowa (as 2013 Chairman), Iowa Seed Fund, Higher Learning Technology and Van Meter Industrial. Prior to Involta, he was CIO of RuffaloCODY and CEO of LIVEware5.

TEN

Phillip Marangella

SUSTAINABLE DATA CENTER SOLUTIONS: FIVE SIMPLE TRUTHS ABOUT A COMPLEX CHALLENGE

Sustainability is Complex

Sometimes a complex task can be simplified and automated. In the not-too-distant past, taking exceptional photographs meant knowing how a camera's aperture, shutter speed, ISO settings, depth-of-field, lens characteristics, and more affected the image the camera would capture. If just one of those settings was misunderstood, there was a good chance that the image would be too dark or too blurry, or too focused on the wrong subject. Today, many phone cameras compete head-to-head with the best cameras in the world to capture memorable images. They allow the photographer to shoot pictures virtually anywhere without thinking about indoor or outdoor conditions. Technology has not replaced high-end photo equipment, but it has made high-quality photography available to billions of people around the world without requiring them to buy a separate camera.

One risk in examples like this is that people may assume that technology can simplify or solve any complex problem. In most cases, however, we need to acknowledge that, while technology can help, the burden of solving complex, real-world problems still lies primarily with humans.

Sustainability is an excellent example of this scenario. For businesses worldwide, there are many facets implied in the term 'sustainability', including air quality, water usage, power generation, ethical behavior, biodiversity, treating employees with dignity, and working with sustainable partners and suppliers.

No one solution can address every facet of the problem, and if not viewed holistically, it is possible to address one component while exacerbating another simultaneously. And while technology can offer ways to improve many conditions of modern life, it can also contribute to many of the concerns typically defined under the umbrella of sustainability.

As a result, before we can effectively tackle the myriad issues involved, we need to recognize the complexity inherent in sustainability and view that complexity as both a cause for concern and an invitation to greater innovation.

In this way, it is easy to see how data centers have historically caused concerns in local markets for their emissions, water usage, impact on biodiversity, and other elements of sustainability. But at the same time, a data center can play a significant role in reducing the effects of technology in a broader sense by employing new cooling solutions, better water usage, cleaner power generation, and more. Improvements at the data center level can have a major ripple effect, extending these improvements to their clients, suppliers, staff, and surrounding communities. But there are very practical, real-world challenges that compound the complexity in ways that humanity has rarely ever had to contend with.

Sustainability is Global

In the 21st century digital economy, data centers are pivot points for data, applications, transactions, security, commerce, and culture. As they have evolved to serve as hubs for more digital activity, their reach has extended to markets virtually everywhere around the globe. To become competitive on the world stage, some markets may embark on a campaign to build data centers without adequate attention to their potential impacts. In other cases, a region with minimal existing infrastructure may be better positioned to deploy sustainable data centers, similar to countries that could build faster mobile networks precisely because they had no legacy landline infrastructure to maintain or decommission. A region, in this case, may have genuine greenfield opportunities to roll out more sustainable solutions.

However, as it progresses, this growth brings both local and global risks. A data center that works ideally for a market like Amsterdam may not be suitable for a market like Mumbai. Power sources and requirements are different, and water usage may have very unique impacts; different tools may be required to reduce and treat Greenhouse Gas (GHG) emissions. Cultural differences also bring diverse perspectives to employee expectations and corporate governance. Sensibilities around concerns about sustainability may have common roots around the globe, but they are unique to each local market or region.

Taken together, the characteristics that make every country, every city unique also compound the complexity of identifying and deploying sustainable solutions.

But looked at historically and with an eye toward the future, that complexity may hold the key to embracing sustainable solutions worldwide.

Let's look at how that can play out for a better, more sustainable future.

Sustainability is Comprehensive

For many years, enterprises felt they needed to build, own, and operate their data centers. There were many reasons for this. For one, enterprise applications were often custom-built or installed locally on enterprise servers and licensed by the number of servers or processors required. For another, the enterprise had its own IT staff, and part of their responsibility was operating the data center itself. Security was a significant concern, and relying on a third party to protect equipment, data, and intellectual property was often a difficult option for enterprises to accept. And not that many years ago, the major data center providers built their data centers in just a few select markets, requiring customers to come to them.

So, until the early years of the new century, there were many disincentives to a more sustainable digital infrastructure. Under the in-house model, data centers tend to generate more waste and consume more power because they are built by and for enterprises whose core competencies are not tied to efficient construction or operations. Outside of the very largest companies in the world, economies of scale could not be applied in ways that mitigated the impacts of enterprise data centers on the land, water, air, power supply, and surrounding communities. If that trend had continued unabated, some of the most dire predictions about data center power consumption and greenhouse gas emissions may have been realized.

So, what changed? Almost everything.

Between 2010 and 2018, data center capacity increased by 600%, internet traffic grew by orders of magnitude, and storage capacity increased by 25x. But data center energy use only grew by 6% over the same period.

As Dr. Jonathan Koomey from Stanford University explains in his June 2021 blog[1] and illustrates in the chart below, the rapid growth in data traffic and transactions does not necessarily result in a corresponding increase in data center energy utilization. Efficiencies introduced into servers, power supplies, cooling, and networking can more than offset higher processing rates, storage, and traffic.

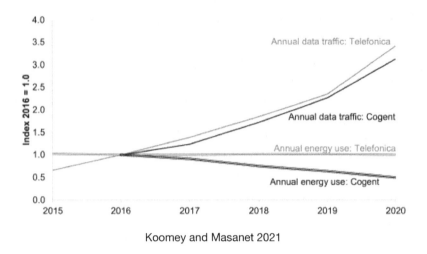

Koomey and Masanet 2021

CPUs and GPUs became more powerful and more efficient at the same time. The growth of cloud services and hyperscale data centers combined to reduce PUE levels—the measure of energy efficiency for a data center—which improved dramatically in the newer, larger facilities built to support a new generation of internet services. Data center providers began building purpose-built facilities, at the right scale, in the right location, optimized for the growing demand in markets around the globe and enterprises were disincentivized from building their own smaller, less efficient premise-based data centers.

The chart below, from Science Magazine,[2] republished by the U.S. Federal Energy Management Program, reinforces this point: data center reliance and utilization keeps rising but new efficiencies tend to more than offset that growth resulting in more effective energy usage.

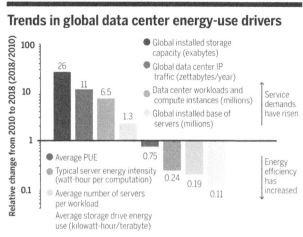

Trends in global data center energy-use drivers

PUE, power usage effectiveness; IP, internet protocol.

Masanet et al. 2020

But that's not the entire answer. During that same period, and still growing today, awareness, sensitivity, and attention to sustainability entered mainstream business conversations. In addition to capacity numbers and network connectivity, customers made efficiency a criterion for choosing a data center provider. Local municipalities and regulators asked hard questions as new data centers were proposed and licensed.

And as data center providers grew and expanded globally, they had lots of reasons to build more efficiently, aided by innovations in power generation, water reuse, GHG emissions management, carbon offsets, biodiversity, and even Data Center Information Management (DCIM) services. And in turn, these elements of sustainability led to a need for transparency and corporate governance because many interested parties were suddenly watching to make sure anyone building or operating a data center was reporting accurate data regarding impacts to the surrounding environment.

As sustainability issues become more prominent in the evaluation and purchasing process, these data providers learned that it's not enough to tackle just one or two elements of the sustainability story. They know that they will be judged on all the criteria combined because, as we noted at the top, sustainability is complex, and its effects are inter-connected.

But it's not enough to have good intentions, or to assume things are improving based on anecdotal evidence, or to take the easy steps that might seem to indicate real progress without any neutral, independent confirmation or guidance.

A Science-Based Approach is Required

What's needed is a rigorous, science-based approach that measures progress consistently across companies and industries, tracking all the elements of a comprehensive sustainability strategy. And these metrics must be known and subscribed to by the data center industry more broadly so that metrics, progress, trends, and trouble spots can be assessed with a shared understanding of what the data tells us.

Fortunately, there are several independent organizations, standards, and certifications that provide the guidance we need to identify, address, and measure the most important elements of sustainability. A partial list is shown below:

- **RE100** – Renewable Energy initiative
- **SBTi** – Science-Based Targets initiative
- **UN Global Compact Ten Principles**
- **UN Sustainability Development Goals** (SDG)
- **ISO 14001** – Standards to assess and control impact on the environment
- **ISO 50001** - For energy management
- **Code Of Conduct for Data Centers** to improve energy efficiency
- **LEED** (Leadership in Energy and Environmental Design)
- **Industry metrics** for Usage Effectiveness measuring Power (PUE), Carbon (CUE), and Water (WUE)

Just as the sustainability efforts of any one business in isolation cannot have a substantial impact, it's also true that, in isolation, any one of these standards and certification initiatives is limited in terms of making a discernible difference. But without these standards and a shared understanding of the measurements and goals, the scope of the problem is harder to identify, and progress is harder to define.

Because of where and how they do business, companies may not join and adopt every one of these and other standards bodies. Still, the key is recognizing that a successful sustainability strategy addresses their concerns and seriously evaluates their guidance.

It's also important to remember that a science-based approach demands transparency. And a key element of transparency is providing information that a global audience can understand and compare using standard terms and data points.

Transparency also allows businesses and organizations to work together, even if they are competitors in other areas. Progress documented by one company can inspire and incent other companies—even competitors—to try harder, do better, and achieve more. Sharing business information with competitors is ill-advised, but sharing sustainability information is critical for the success of global initiatives and local action.

While it's true that customers consider a data center provider's sustainability track record when purchasing capacity and services, transparency demands that each company's goals, progress, achievements, and efforts still to be completed are reported and published for public consumption. Concrete data points, real-world examples, solutions that work are all part of any credible, reliable, transparent sustainability report. Customers demand nothing less, partners expect to rely on it, and businesses will compare their efforts to those of their competitors.

In the End, Sustainability is About Tracking Results

After all the discussion and planning and data gathering, in the end, sustainability is best measured by results. These results should include practical, real-world steps that are taken to mitigate the impacts of any business on customers, people, and the planet.

When we look at effective results, we cannot ignore the single-lane solutions that improve one category alone. It is certainly possible to make significant strides in reducing carbon emissions, water usage, GHG, power efficiency, or any single topic under the sustainability umbrella.

For example, a single data center in one market might take significant steps to reduce carbon emissions. That's a good thing. But by itself, its contribution to a more sustainable planet and future is not substantial. And, in some cases, the effort and energy put into that single solution might end up causing negative impacts in other areas that more than offset the positive effects.

Let's look at a few examples of sustainable data center solutions that can contribute to a strategic view by delivering results that combine to have a real, measurable impact, both locally and globally.

- **Water Usage**: In many parts of the world, one of the biggest causes for concern with new data centers is their use of water for cooling, often taking water that might otherwise be used for local drinking water, agriculture, or other everyday purposes. There are an increasing number of options that data center providers might adopt to help alleviate these concerns, such as: recycling water so that it is cleansed of any deposits, dirt, or chemicals; and reusing large amounts of any water used by the data center. Alternative cooling methods are emerging that can help reduce water usage from day-one. And servers that can operate at higher temperatures help data centers run more efficiently, requiring less cooling than traditional equipment. In fact, locating data centers in places where temperatures are naturally cooler can help because, as noted at the outset, sustainability is global and the right solutions in one market may differ from the right solutions in another.

- **Power Sourcing**: For many years now, data centers have been viewed as taking electricity from local and regional power grids, but today some alternatives help alleviate or even reverse the power flow. Geothermal, solar, wind, and other emerging energy sources are powering data centers in markets around the globe, taking advantage of local resources and in many cases, returning power back to the local or regional grid. Providers and hyperscalers are also exploring undersea data centers to drive more efficient cooling and reduced energy consumption, which, like any of these new opportunities, is limited to certain markets where such projects are more feasible. But the broader lesson is, data center innovation itself is a key contributor to solving the challenges of a more sustainable future.

- **Biodiversity**: As with water usage, biodiversity is important to both sustainability and, in layman's terms, to being a good neighbor. Maintaining as much of the natural surrounding plant growth as possible, minimizing both the disruption to native species and the introduction of invasive species, and ensuring that the buildings do not contribute to problems with water run-off or air quality are all components of a strong biodiversity initiative, from saving water to saving bees.

- **Waste Removal:** The time-honored slogan "Reduce, Reuse, Recycle", created to encourage less waste among consumers, also applies to data centers and other sustainability-sensitive industries. In most cases, the materials that need to be reduced, reused, and recycled originate outside the data center and have a defined shelf life before being discarded or replaced. But a critical step is to track the recycling of e-waste — old computers, monitors, printers, and more — to reduce landfill deliveries and allow manufacturers and repair shops to take advantage of recycled materials.

- **Downstream Effects**: One important area for making an impact is addressing downstream effects of decisions made in data center operations. For example, a Data Center Information Management (DCIM) application that allows customers, vendors, partners, and operations staff to perform business and technical tasks remotely can significantly reduce travel previously required for those same tasks. Air travel and car travel, once routine for managing data center assets, can become an infrequent activity, offering downstream benefits not always ascribed to a data center but clearly attributable as part of a global process chain.

We won't list every component of a comprehensive strategy, but it's important to note that a strategy that takes all this into consideration, and includes carbon, GHG, and other crucial elements, along with the unique characteristics of data center scale and market location is much more likely to provide more measurable, consequential results.

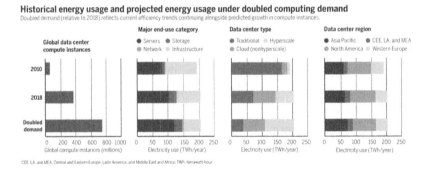

Historical energy usage and projected energy usage under doubled computing demand
Doubled demand (relative to 2018) reflects current efficiency trends continuing alongside predicted growth in compute instances.

Masanet et al. 2020

In short, when we take a more holistic view of sustainability, it becomes easier to see the problem areas and the incentives for taking the proper steps to improve efficiency, waste, power generation, cooling, environment, and tracking for different locations around the globe. Some challenges are regional, some are the product of scaling, and others are affected by resource availability or recycling and disposal options in different markets. But combined, they all offer opportunities to empower data centers to act as catalysts and contributors to a more sustainable world.

Conclusion

Sustainability works best when viewed comprehensively, with a reliance on recognized standards and science that can quantify the results both locally and globally. Ultimately, the collective results of industry-wide efforts promise to substantially affect our climate, our resources, our communities, and people around the globe.

Data centers are pivotal elements of the digital economy and the internet infrastructure. They touch everything, data, content, cloud, networks, applications, security, the power grid, undersea cables, charging stations, and more. Their performance impacts the sharing of data, applications, cultures, commerce, content, and knowledge globally, so their importance cannot be overstated.

But that importance does not outweigh the impacts of data centers on our natural resources or communities. While there have been missteps in the past, more and more data center providers today are participating in and complying with standards bodies and organizations that track, measure, and certify the industry's progress.

And their importance is precisely what makes it so imperative that data centers take a leading role in developing and deploying sustainable solutions that are global, comprehensive, science-based, and focused on results.

The execution is complex, but the key is remembering that the goal is simple: building a strong, sustainable future.

---

1. Koomey, Jonathan, and Eric Masanet. 2021. "Does not compute: Avoiding pitfalls in assessing the Internet's energy and carbon impacts." Joule. June 24,

2021. https://doi.org/10.1016/j.joule.2021.05.007.

2. Masanet, Eric, Arman Shehabi, Nuoa Lei, Sarah Smith, and Jonathan Koomey. 2020. "Recalibrating global data center energy-use estimates." *Science* 367 (6481), 984-986. DOI: 10.1126/science.aba3758.

About the Author

PHILLIP MARANGELLA

Phillip has nearly 25 years of international marketing, strategy, and business development experience working in the Data Center, Telecom and Technology sectors for leading service providers. Prior to joining EdgeConneX, he most recently worked for Equinix in various capacities in both marketing and business development. In addition, Phillip had stints at Coresite, Verizon Business, MCI, Nortel, Globalstar, and Satphone.

Currently serving as the Chief Marketing and Product Officer at EdgeConneX, Phillip is focused on developing, evangelizing and executing the marketing and product strategy, ecosystem development for the company. He also serves on the marketing advisory boards for Lokker, Salute Mission Critical and Infrastructure Masons. Phillip leverages his experience within the telecommunications industry to accelerate EdgeConneX' commitment to greener data.

Phillip won the prestigious Infrastructure Masons champion awards for both Diversity & Inclusion and Education in 2021 for his work developing and mentoring the HBCU Capstone Programs. He has also led initiatives in support of veterans and women, and he was ranked as a top 10 marketing executive in the industry by DataCentre magazine.

ELEVEN

Raul Martynek

STRIKING THE BALANCE: MEETING THE GROWING DEMAND FOR POWER WHILE MITIGATING THE EFFECTS OF CLIMATE CHANGE

A Commitment to Greener Data (and Whiter Mountains) in the Future

When I was approached to contribute to this book, I was flattered at first … and then I was thrilled. The very premise of the book—how the data center industry can become more environmentally friendly—completely aligns with my personal views as well as my ideas for how DataBank should evolve and grow. I truly believe that climate change is the single biggest issue humankind is facing today. As a father of four children who have always enjoyed the outdoors—especially skiing—I've already seen the effects of climate change, and unless we act now, it's only going to get worse. I also believe that climate change could be devastating to various segments of the global population, especially those who are economically disadvantaged.

Clearly, so many other political, economic, socio-cultural, and technological issues confront us today, and while these are concerning, hard to solve, and deserving of our time and focus, I believe climate change should be at the top of the list. It is extremely difficult to address and will require collaboration, agreement, and new innovations from citizens across the world. If we don't get it right, climate change is the one issue that could potentially destroy the entire planet.

At the same time, I'm the CEO of DataBank, one of the largest data center providers in the United States. We have more than 60+ data centers in 27+ different markets on two continents and are committed to our customers' success when it comes to providing colocation hosting and the related services they need to power their computer infrastructures and serve their customers. The demand for computing and data is only going to grow, so it's clear that DataBank will continue to consume power.

Admittedly, our mission could seem to be at odds with our desire to minimize our overall environmental impact. Yet, this doesn't mean that we can't take the long view and do all we can now to use less power, increase our overall efficiency, and always consider new alternatives and emerging technologies to become as sustainable as possible. I'm proud of the strides and early accomplishments we've already made, but we're not satisfied.

We're starting to take steps in the right direction. When I became DataBank's CEO in 2016, we didn't yet have an Environmental, Social, and Governance (ESG) program in place. We developed and implemented this program, and we included newly formed leadership positions that will ensure that ESG becomes a vital part of our overall business. We view ESG just like any other important part of the business. In the same way finance, operations, management, and other functional areas drive DataBank's business, we'll make important decisions through an ESG lens, especially related to climate change. Furthermore, we'll continue to refine this approach with short- and long-term objectives, such as including energy efficiency goals as part of our operations teams' MBOs.

DataBank is fortunate to work with several institutional investors who share a similar vision when it comes to our use of power and cooling technologies (More to come on this below) and who encourage us to become as sustainable as possible, now and into the future. Our lead investor, DigitalBridge, has established a benchmark mandate that all its portfolio companies–including DataBank–must become 100% carbon neutral by 2030. We have much work to do.

Today's Challenges are Truly Opportunities in Disguise

Today, data centers consume tremendous amounts of electricity to power their servers, storage equipment, back-ups, and power-cooling infrastructure. U.S.-based data centers use more than 90 billion kilowatt-hours of electricity a year, a number that is expected to double every four years.[1]

Additionally, *The New York Times* reported that data centers around the world use more than 30 billion watts of electricity–the equivalent of the energy generation from 30 nuclear power plants. The United States accounts for approximately one-third of that consumption.[2]

It's a real concern because the entire industry will continue to consume more power. Nevertheless, we still need to focus on ensuring the power we do consume is as efficient as possible and includes a wider array of renewable energy sources. In particular, consider that current electricity production processes, such as coal-powered power stations, produce excessive amounts of carbon dioxide. To me, it all adds up to a conundrum for the whole industry to consider: If everyone is concerned with climate change and the possible destruction of the planet, why aren't we all doing everything possible to reverse these negative effects?

There are other factors in play. Because DataBank is in so many markets, we don't always have the full control we like to have. While hyperscale cloud providers have the advantage of plunking down in just a few regions, we face highly regulated local situations. For example, we don't always have the advantage of buying 2,000 acres in rural locations, or even the option to work with local windmills or solar farms. Unfortunately, under current regulatory, financial, and physical conditions, these are not real-istic scenarios in our urban facilities and sites.

While it's fair to say that some organizations still lag behind the more progressive climate change champions, or even resist the need to change their practices, many of the larger, more modern companies are now demonstrating leadership by being vocal proponents of efforts to address and mitigate climate change. When it comes to data centers, the majority of people involved—including C-suite executives and customers alike—are concerned that the power demands of our digital infrastructure are having a major, detrimental impact on the environment.

As a result, increasing demand is forcing data center operators to seek new ways to minimize the impact, even just to remain competitive by marketplace standards.

Smart Chillers, Server Loads, and Sustainable Energy Sources: Ways to Bring Down Energy Consumption Now

Thankfully, technology advancements have given U.S. data center operators additional hope and the opportunity to advance sustainability. These innovations allow us to decrease energy consumption in our facilities while reducing costs through several smart moves in the near future.

One example: Investing in energy-efficient commercial chiller equipment that offers more competitive energy performance and proven reliability. Smart-building technology providers now offer advanced chiller equipment that uses better types of refrigerants and is optimized to significantly reduce average annual electricity consumption. For example, the latest air-cooled chilling systems can now enhance uptime and reliability as well as energy performance, without the need for traditional water-based evaporative systems.

We believe data center operators should also consider using free-cooling chiller solutions that include variable speed drives and evaporative cooling technologies for even better energy efficiency. Variable speed drives offer a clear advantage over a motor that must always run at full speed, even though this level is not required for most applications. These drives can control the frequency of starting and stopping the motor as well as its speed, which saves significant amounts of energy and reduces overall costs. Digital resources and analytics are other ways to further optimize energy use.

Clearly in a typical data center, server loads will vary throughout each day. A smart solution is to monitor the energy consumption patterns to allow data center managers to configure the optimal use of their resources. It also lets them identify and diagnose equipment problems and take proactive steps to fix them.

At DataBank, we also believe it is time to challenge the convention of operating at low temperatures, usually 68-71°F. While many old-school businesses still profess a preference for cold air conditioners, there is new and emerging research that shows we can actually run data centers at higher temperatures than we currently do, (for example, three to five degrees hotter) without any significant sacrifices in system reliability. This could deliver additional power savings related to power consumption for the chillers.

Sustainable energy sources should be considered to power data centers whenever possible. Singapore recently announced plans to quadruple its solar deployment by 2025 and is now working toward deploying at least two gigawatt-peak (GWp) of solar–approximately three percent of the country's total projected energy consumption by 2030. Among other highlights, this effort includes a massive floating solar farm that covers the size of 45 football fields and includes 122,000 panels.[3]

The combination of these factors can help certain customers, such as single tenant hyperscale cloud data centers, to reduce the overall use of power. Temperature control can be an advantage, but the ability to right-size their entire infrastructure from the start also helps create efficiencies and avoid having to add new infrastructure to accommodate future growth.

DataBank shares all of these concerns and would like to do all we can to improve, and we are very aware of our environmental impact. We have continuously adapted our facilities and overall operations–our effort to leave no stone unturned–in our search to make the most of our environmental responsibility.

Data centers focus tremendous amounts of time seeking the most efficient use of power. The biggest factor in power consumption is one over which data centers have little control: manufacturers' designs resulting in customers' hardware. The second biggest factor in power consumption is power usage effectiveness (PUE) – an industry-standard measurement of how efficiently a data center cools the waste energy coming off computers. This is an area where data centers have much room to innovate and find improvements.

We are considering and pursuing the following alternatives.

Renewable Power Sources

Our Indianapolis data centers were the first in the industry to be 100% powered by renewable sources. Two of our data centers moved 100% of their combined electricity usage into a voluntary program that directs Indianapolis Power and Light to purchase renewable energy from wind farms and other midwestern facilities.

Through that program, DataBank will offset the carbon dioxide emissions by the equivalent of 3,321 passenger cars driven in one year or 84 railroad cars of coal burned. Participants in the Indianapolis program now help support the development of additional renewable energy sources, further helping reduce reliance on fossil-fueled power.

In addition, one of our Minneapolis data centers is 100% powered by renewable wind sources as part of the Wellspring program offered by Dakota Electric. Through this program, DataBank will purchase enough wind-generated power to cover all of this Minneapolis data center's power requirements for the next five years.

Since pioneering these efforts to procure 100% of our energy at these sites from renewable power, DataBank has continued to enroll additional sites in similar programs where available, including those in Illinois, Texas, and New Jersey.

Economizer Cooling Strategies

Thousands of servers in a data center can—and do—generate tremendous heat, which then needs to be removed in order to keep sensitive electronic systems running. Massive air conditioning systems are the primary mechanism for this, but they consume significant amounts of power. In colder climates and cooler seasons, the use of naturally cold external air helps reduce the overall reliance on air conditioning compressor units and reduces power consumption, a process called economization.

DataBank currently operates several economizer systems in many of our data centers in locations such as Dallas, Minneapolis, Atlanta, and Salt Lake City. Highly precise sensors measure the outside air temperature and humidity, and if conditions are appropriate, they open air dampeners to allow outside air to cool the facility.

The system closes those air dampeners when the conditions require a return to mechanical cooling. The whole process is like opening a window at your house on a nice day, but it also offers fully autonomous capabilities with sophisticated sensing and control sequences that maintain strict temperature and humidity parameters.

Environmentally Friendly Refrigerants

Air conditioning systems require refrigerant chemicals that can have a negative impact on our atmosphere —by depleting ozone and further contributing to global warming. A refrigerant's Global Warming Potential (GWP) is a measurement of a chemical's contribution to global warming and enables comparison between different options. In the past, a refrigerant called R22 has been the most commonly used chemical in air conditioning systems and had both a high GWP as well as a destructive impact on ozone.

At DataBank, we have switched the vast majority of our mechanical cooling systems to an R410a refrigerant, which is the most efficient and environmentally friendly coolant available. Additionally, we are exploring the use of another chemical called R32. Both R23 and R410 have largely replaced R22 due to their lack of ozone impact and the fact they have a lower GWP.

Heat Recycling

While venting data center waste heat into the atmosphere may be efficient, we soon realized that this heat had value in other infrastructures.

For example, DataBank's ATL1 data center in Atlanta hosts the Georgia Tech liquid-cooled supercomputer, which offers high performance computing to the institution's faculty, research scientists, graduate students, and academic and government affiliates. A water-cooled door chilling system in this data center gives Data-Bank the ability to scale up to 100kW per cabinet without having to take up additional space for cooling. The heat and waste energy from the supercomputer is transferred to the chilled water, which then reaches 90 degrees and is supplied to the building's boilers for use by other tenants.

Greener Backup Systems

Back-up power systems are a critical component of any data center operation and keep mission-critical systems and applications up and running, even when there is an interruption to utility-provided power. These backup systems need to be reliable, scalable, efficient, and use as little space as possible.

Advanced, three-phase UPS battery systems provide the most popular option, delivering smart, dependable power in a compact format. However, their use of lead-acid chemicals is not environmentally friendly, and they need to be replaced periodically.

To minimize this impact, DataBank has turned to an innovative combination of UPS batteries with flywheels. A flywheel system stores energy mechanically in the form of kinetic energy by spinning a mass at high speed. When used in conjunction with a battery-powered UPS system, the flywheel systems are affected first during a power outage. This preserves the battery for use in longer-term outages and minimizes discharge cycles to prolong overall battery life.

Onsite Power Generation

Relying exclusively on utility power means a data center's power costs will rise as overall demand rises. Being able to offset those costs at peak times with onsite power generation is a way to reduce total costs while improving overall efficiency.

We accomplished this in the previously mentioned Atlanta data center. We partnered with a local utility (Georgia Power) to deploy a 1.5MW microgrid to support Georgia Tech's High Performance Computing Center (HPCC), which is housed in the Atlanta data center. The microgrid runs in parallel to Georgia Power's grid as an additional power source. It senses power consumption and can export power to the facility in an emergency or simply at peak times to save costs.

The installation includes fuel cells, battery storage, diesel generators, and a natural gas generator, but it is also adaptive to new and additional distributed energy sources. It will be able to accommodate microturbines, solar panels, and electric vehicle chargers in the future.

Being the Change

We're all in this together. When it comes to accommodating the growing demand for data-driven computing while minimizing the effects of climate change, the entire data center industry needs to continue to come together and play a proactive role in shaping the best possible future.

We already see evidence of this today. Whether it's the idea of tax incentives from municipalities to encourage the development of alternative energy sources, or more collaboration between data center operators and utilities for even more efficient energy supplies and use, we're already making important progress. Yet, we'll all need to do even more as we go and continue to pursue additional innovations and options. It's in our collective best interests and translates into real-world implications for all of us. After all, I'm looking forward to hiking and skiing with my family—now and into the future—so I will assure that DataBank continues to do all it can to support these important goals.

---

1. Danilak, Rado. 2017. "Why Energy Is A Big and Rapidly Growing Problem for Data Centers." *Forbes*, December 15, 2017. https://www.forbes.com/sites/forbestechcouncil/2017/12/15/why-energy-is-a-big-and-rapidly-growing-problem-for-data-centers/?sh=3b3c60415a30.
2. Glanz, James. 2012. "Power, Pollution and the Internet." *The New York Times*, September 23, 2012. https://www.nytimes.com/2012/09/23/technology/data-centers-waste-vast-amounts-of-energy-belying-industry-image.html.
3. Lin, Chen. 2021. "Singapore Unveils One of the World's Biggest Floating Solar Panel Farms." *Reuters*, July 14, 2021. https://www.reuters.com/business/energy/singapore-unveils-one-worlds-biggest-floating-solar-panel-farms-2021-07-14/.

About the Author

RAUL MARTYNEK

Raul Martynek is a 20+ year veteran in the telecom and Internet Infrastructure sector and has served as Chief Executive Officer of DataBank since June of 2016. He most recently served as a Senior Advisor for Digital Bridge Holdings LLC. Prior to Digital Bridge, he served as Chief Executive Officer for New Jersey-based data center and managed services operator Net Access, LLC, and prior to Net Access, he was the CEO of Voxel dot Net, Inc., a global managed hosting and cloud company, which was acquired by Internap Network Services Corp. in early 2012.

Mr. Martynek also served as the Chief Restructuring Officer of Smart Telecom, a Dublin-based fiber carrier. Before that, he evaluated investment opportunities in the telecommunications and Internet sector as a Senior Advisor at Plainfield Asset Management, a $4B hedge fund. Mr. Martynek also spent 13 years with telecom and Internet provider InfoHighway Communications Corp, first as a Chief Operating Officer of Eureka Networks and then as President and Chief Executive Officer of InfoHighway, acquired by Broadview Networks in 2007. Mr. Martynek earned a Bachelor of Arts in Political Science from Binghamton University and a Master's Degree in International Affairs from Columbia University School of International and Public Affairs.

TWELVE

Dean Nelson

DEFINING THE DIGITAL INFRASTRUCTURE INDUSTRY

"If you can measure it, you can improve it".
—Lord Kelvin

I have been in Digital Infrastructure for 32 years now. My journey started in 1989 on a sunny California morning in Milpitas. It was my first day at Sun Microsystems, and it was also my 21st birthday. This was a new chapter in my life filled with the excitement of my first real job in one of the most beautiful places in the world. After completing my associates degree in electronics at DeVry, a trade school in Phoenix Arizona, Sun hired half my graduating class and told us to move to Silicon Valley! I was going to be an electronic technician on the manufacturing line debugging component-level failures on servers and storage. The funny thing was that I had no idea what Silicon Valley was, and didn't know anything about computer hardware, operating systems, networks, software or data centers. I was a complete newbie. I spent 17 years at Sun employed twice between 1989-2009. I joined a startup company in 2000 called Allegro Networks. I then spent seven years at Ebay, Inc. running global foundational services for their portfolio of companies including PayPal, Stubhub, and dozens of other acquisitions. In 2016 I went on to join Uber to help them hyperscale their digital infrastructure to keep up with unprecedented growth. I left Uber on my 51st birthday—30 years exactly as an end user.

When I look back, I now realize that I had driven $10B in infrastructure projects across three continents. Playing a part of building the foundation for the internet of everything is really cool. From my perspective, I learned technology, business, management, operations, sustainability and strategy at the University of Sun Microsystems. It was a trial by fire, but incredibly fulfilling intellectually and personally. Sun was an amazing place with talented and passionate people fueling the infrastructure for the digital age, and it prepared me to play my part in expanding what we know today as Digital Infrastructure. I also formed a professional association called Infrastructure Masons (iMasons) to unite the builders of the digital age across some very important areas in our burgeoning industry: Education, Diversity & Inclusion, Technology, and Sustainability.

My chapter is focused on how we as an industry can leverage our community and technology to do our part to tackle climate change. Like any project, it is important to know where you're starting from, what the rules are, and how you can measure progress. The challenge is that to date we have not defined or structured that information for the Digital Infrastructure industry. Companies and individuals are doing incredible work, but it can be difficult to show that the sum is greater than the parts.

The Size of Our Industry

For more than a decade, I have watched, read, and been involved in hundreds of discussions about the size of our industry. How many data centers are there? How are they classified? How much capacity is built? How much power is used? Who is using it? How efficient is it? What's the carbon footprint? How fast is it growing? All of these are very important questions, but we never seem to have clear, defensible answers. Most are estimates based on extrapolations of data that only see part of the picture.

The last large industry debate I was involved in was in London in 2019. Christian Belady, Amber Caramella, Gary Cook, Heather Dooley, Dave Johnson, Bill Kleyman, Martin Lynch, Patrick Ohlund, George Rockett, Eddie Schutter, Noelle Walsh, and many more participated in panels at Data Centre Dynamics as well as the iMasons' member summit and Advisory Council session.

The result? Our estimates for global data center energy consumption ranged from 1% to 10%, with many assuming it is below 2%. The point is, there is no definitive measure that any could agree upon. On the other hand, hyperscalers like Apple, Amazon, Google, Meta, and Microsoft have accurate numbers since they build and operate their own data centers. They know the capacity, consumption, and efficiency down to the second because it matters to their bottom line.

In the beginning of 2021, Synergy claimed there are 600 hyper scale data centers, which had doubled since 2015.[1] In November of 2021, Bill Kleyman reported that traditional data centers have shrunk from 50% to less than 25% of the market replaced by hyperscale data centers growth.[2] That development continues with gigawatts of new capacity in the pipeline.

The sessions in London highlighted that many companies have made significant progress individually, but the primary question remains. Data centers are more efficient and sustainable, and the world is more dependent upon them than ever, but we cannot quantify by how much.

In my opinion, the debate continues because we have not agreed on how to scope the digital infrastructure industry nor established a taxonomy that clearly classifies how to measure it. Without these, we cannot set a baseline and show progress.

In the summer of 2021, I worked with Rob Aldrich, the chair of the Infrastructure Masons Sustainability Committee, as well as other industry experts to tackle this problem. Over the last six months we researched, discussed, debated, and ultimately aligned on a proposal.

Defining Digital Infrastructure

I started Infrastructure Masons in 2016 to unite the builders of the digital age. Our members represent some of the largest portfolios in the world. They build and operate the foundation of the internet of everything. Their portfolios are the engines that enable consumption of digital services worldwide. Yet if we limit the measurement to enterprise and hyperscale facilities, we are missing more than half of the global consumption. We found that the traditional definition of a data center was too narrow. We expanded the aperture to include all elements that make up the infrastructure that delivers digital services, i.e. the IT equipment that processes and stores data, the facilities that house that equipment, and the networks that connect them all. This led to our first definition in the project.

What is Digital Infrastructure?

Digital Infrastructure is a collection of data center locations that deliver electronic services to people and machines.

We agreed that Digital infrastructure is made up of unique locations that have specific addresses just like the street address at your home or a network address on the internet. Duplication of these addresses would cause conflicts and potentially double counting of consumption. Like apps in the app store, those services constantly change with nearly unlimited permutations over time, but they all consume infrastructure capacity. We kept this definition simple and concise to ensure that both technical and non-technical people could understand.

Once we defined Digital Infrastructure, we needed to answer the next question:

What are Data Centers?

Data Centers are real estate locations that house IT equipment to process, store, and transmit data.

We've established that Digital Infrastructure is a collection of data centers and that each data center is a real estate location with a unique address. These locations house IT equipment that do one or more of these things—process data, store data, and/or transmit data. Every data center in the world is covered with this definition.

Finally, we needed to answer one more question to be able to establish a baseline of global consumption:

How are Data Centers Classified?

Data Centers are classified into three primary categories—providers, networks, and crypto.

We held five different iMasons working sessions to review and fine-tune the structure. Data center classifications and their definitions were the largest debate.

Providers include data centers that deliver services to themselves, others, or both. For example, Cloud, Hyperscale, Enterprise, Colocation, and Edge. This category was understood and agreed upon.

Networks include data centers that operate as carrier hotels, internet exchanges, fixed networks, and mobile networks. This category sparked numerous debates as carrier hotels and internet exchanges are usually intermingled with enterprise, colo, cloud and even hyperscale data centers. Our assertion is that a real estate location can have a unique address yet house multiple tenants such as a restaurant on the ground floor and apartments on the upper floors. The key is to ensure that the real estate location with a unique address accounts for all types of classes without duplication. Meaning, a data center could house both providers and networks in the same address, but consumption of power is specific to each category in that building.

Crypto includes all crypto mining and blockchain services. This is a new category that has grown rapidly over the last five years primarily due to bitcoin mining. While blockchain is the base technology, bitcoin represents over 80% of consumption today. Adding crypto to Digital Infrastructure was the most controversial part of our proposal. The reason we kept it as a stand-alone category was due to growth forecasts. Crypto power consumption could surpass the other categories as services based on blockchain continue to expand. Purists do not believe crypto should be a data center category as it does not fit into the traditional definition of data centers;. e.g. crypto deployments do not have resiliency built in—no generators, UPS, or redundancy to protect from faults. Our assertion is that crypto sites deliver electronic services to people and machines just like providers and networks. The difference is that they do not require the same level of resilience in the data center design based on the distributed nature of blockchain.

The most important element of this taxonomy is that every data center site will have a unique identifier—i.e. an address. This is critical as we will not be able to establish a baseline and measure progress if there is overlap or duplication. This approach already works for many other things in our society—every real estate location has a unique street address regardless of its location, size or use. The internet is based on TCP/IP which ensures that every device has a unique address in order to communicate.

Energy Consumption & Calculation

Based on the taxonomy outlined above, we can now see Digital Infrastructure in its entirety. For our work, we first want to baseline power capacity and consumption. Statista reported in 2021 that there are 7 million data centers globally.[3] Each has a unique street address ranging from mega data center sites exceeding 1GW of capacity to micro edge deployments on the corners of streets drawing less than 1kW of power. These 7 million data centers represent 105GW of power capacity. In 2021, they consumed 594TWhs of energy globally. That represents 2.4% of global energy consumption.

594TWhs of consumption translates to 67,808MW of capacity that is consumed at any given moment. To put that in perspective, water processing and delivery consumes 13% of global energy. Digital Infrastructure consumes 2.4%.

Cambridge Bitcoin Electricity Consumption Index (CBE-CI.org)[4] reported that bitcoin dropped from 140TWhs to 115TWhs when China banned crypto mining in Q2 of 2021. That capacity is currently migrating from China to many other regions including the US, EMEA, and LATAM. Crypto consumption will continue to increase significantly. As of the printing of this book, CBECI reported Crypto had risen back to 141 TWhs as much of the China capacity has found a new home and additional capacity has been added.

LIVE

Bitcoin network power demand
updated every 24 hours

Theoretical lower bound	Estimated	Theoretical upper bound
	16.10	
6.04	GW	**40.42**
GW		GW

Annualised consumption

52.97	141.10	354.31
TWh	TWh	TWh

© Cambridge Bitcoin Electricity Consumption Index

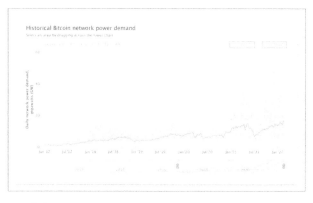

Historical Bitcoin network power demand

© Cambridge Bitcoin Electricity Consumption Index

Efficiency

Energy consumption is only one part of the story. We made some very conservative estimates on utilization to back into the total global capacity number. If we assume that networks and providers continuously utilize 60% of their built capacity and crypto utilizes 97% of their capacity, we have an average of 65% utilization globally. That means 68GW of consumption translates to 105GW of built capacity. That leaves 37GW of capacity that is unused. We applied an average build cost of $7M/ MW for networks, $5M/MW for providers and $250k/MW for crypto. Based on these costs, 37GW of unused capacity translates to over $220B of investment dollars that are not yielding returns and more than $20B in revenue opportunities left on the table. While some capacity is needed to be ahead of demand for rapid growth categories such as cloud and social media, many agree that utilization is actually lower than our estimates leaving even more stranded capacity. Bottom line, there is a significant opportunity to increase efficiency and yield from investments.

Chris Crosby, CEO of Compass Data Centers, raised another efficiency area that should be considered: utility transmission and over-generation. First, many large colo, hyperscale, and cloud providers invest in substations to serve their properties avoiding up to 20% of transmission losses. Second, many renewable energy sources overproduce capacity due to their variability. Technology to store this capacity cost effectively at grid scale has not been achieved yet but it is expected in the near future. Today, some providers are optimizing workloads to utilize this over-generation as it happens. Crypto mining located at the generation source, like wind and solar farms, can ramp up becoming carbon negative during over-generation and avoid wasting that energy. Cloud and edge providers are applying carbon-aware kubernetes to dynamically move workloads to low-carbon areas to achieve the same thing.

Growth

Correlating input from data center equipment providers, colo, providers, construction firms, and edge capacity reports shows that 20,000MW of new capacity will be built in hyperscale, colo and edge by the end of 2024. That growth will be led by India, Africa, and Latin America. One of the concerns with this growth is that we will be perpetuating the low utilization model across the globe. This is not sustainable economically or ecologically.

Sustainability

On Earth Day in 2020, iMasons launched a unified Sustainability Vision: Every Click Improves the Future.[5] We believe that Digital Infrastructure contributes to society and the economy without harming the planet.

This vision was written to support sustainable business practices applying a triple bottom line—people, profit, and planet. Environmental sustainability is the responsibility to conserve natural resources and protect global ecosystems to support health and wellbeing, now and in the future. Sustainability is a huge topic. For this effort, we are focusing on establishing a global baseline for data center power capacity and consumption to measure the industry's carbon footprint.

Our industry accounts for 2.4% of global power consumption,

yet we are unable to show our carbon footprint—good or bad. By establishing the taxonomy for our industry, we can enable real-time carbon accounting for Digital Infrastructure. This requires industry buy-in to measure embodied carbon and carbon attributed to consumption of power to deliver digital services.

We have three proposals that are enabled by the new taxonomy.

Digital Infrastructure: Source Power

Carbon tracking of source energy attributed to each unique data center location.

Every data center location has one or more power feeds to enable the data center to run. Each of those power feeds has a carbon footprint associated with the source. This is the easiest measurement as most data centers have this tracked in real time.

Digital Infrastructure: Carbon Sticker

Carbon Stickers showing embodied carbon for data centers facilities, ME&P components and IT equipment housed in those data centers.

Martin Lynch, CEO of Pure Data Centers raised this brilliant idea at the iMasons End User Forum in October 2021. Each food product that you buy in a store has a nutrition facts label.[6] That breaks down what is in that food product, e.g. serving size, calories, percent of daily value, and nutrients. We propose an equivalent "Carbon Facts Sticker" that outlines embedded carbon for data center buildings, ME&P equipment, and IT equipment housed in those data centers.

Carbon Facts

1234 Internet Blvd, Building 1A, Anywhere, USA 99999
Commissioned: 2013. Useful Life: 262,800 MWh
Cabon Label: July 12, 2021
Unit Size: 10 MW critical, 2.5MW reserve per data center
Data Center Units 12.5MW (23,456 MTCO2e/kWh)

Amount of MTCO2e per MWh

Embodied Carbon   1,877

Materials	**39%**
Products	**61%**

% Data Center Embodied Carbon	
Base Construction	**38%**
Concrete (MTCO2e/kWh)	46%
Steel (MTCO2e/kWh)	23%
Copper (MTCO2e/kWh)	18%
Other (MTCO2e/kWh)	13%
Base Electrical	**24%**
Switch Gear (MTCO2e/kWh)	12%
Generators (MTCO2e/kWh)	9%
Distribution (PDU/RPP/Busway/etc) (MTCO2e/kWh)	29%
Pipework & Copper (MTCO2e/kWh)	33%
Other (MTCO2e/kWh)	17%
Base Cooling	**18%**
Plant (MTCO2e/kWh)	56%
Data Halls (MTCO2e/kWh)	24%
Fittings & Pipework (MTCO2e/kWh)	12%
Other (MTCO2e/kWh)	8%
Base Ancillary	**9%**
Fire Detection / Supression (MTCO2e/kWh)	25%
Leak Detection (MTCO2e/kWh)	11%
VESDA (MTCO2e/kWh)	9%
Other (MTCO2e/kWh)	55%

% Data Center Embodied Carbon	
Data Center Projects	
Base: 4MW, 8/22/2013	33%
Expansion: 3MW,12/13/2018	24%
Expansion: 2.5MW, 9/01/2019	21%
Retrofit: 3MW, 6/30/2021	24%

Infrastructure Masons carbon baseline taxonomy proposal for demonstration purposes
only. Categories, components, and values will change as industry alignment is achieved.

https://imasons.org/climateaccord

The Carbon Facts Sticker included here is for illustrative purposes to show the concept of applying this to a data center. The serving size is one data center building. Calories equate to metric tons of carbon (MTCO2e) for each element in building that data center. For example, how much embodied carbon is attributed to building the data center or manufacturing, delivering and installing a UPS, generator or switchgear? How do you attribute carbon to data center retrofit and expansion projects? This also can be applied in the same manner to any equipment in the data center. Each UPS, generator, switchgear, server, network switch, etc should have their own Carbon Facts Sticker. The combination of the building and its components will represent the total embodied carbon footprint for that location. Additional carbon will be applied to this data center carbon sticker as new equipment comes in and old equipment goes out and the data center is modified to deliver services over its lifetime. Bottom line, each device and building has a carbon origin and a unique history that should be measurable.

This proposal is to get people thinking and manufacturers and builders to dive in. Movement is already happening as industry leaders like Schneider Electric and Vertiv are actively pursuing this concept for their products. Molg, a startup company, has also developed an open standard called the OriginMark that supports traceability of products including embodied carbon. This could be a methodology that our industry could leverage to dynamically track the carbon history of devices and data centers. The specifics of this concept will continue to evolve as more companies join the cause.

Digital Infrastructure: Real Time Tracking

Embodied Carbon Stickers plus source power would enable real time global tracking of the digital infrastructure industry's carbon footprint.

Carbon Stickers for the facility and devices in those facilities can now be added to the carbon associated with the power consumed to deliver those electronic services. The result is real-time accounting for carbon for each data center location. But we want to take this one step further and standardize on a unit of measure that does not care about what services are being consumed in the data center. For example, every data center has network connectivity. That connectivity has associated packets that are transmitted and received in the data center. Those packets would have a fully-loaded carbon tax based on embodied carbon tracked in the Carbon Stickers and carbon associated with source power consumed by devices in the data center. Since the digital infrastructure taxonomy ensures every data center has a unique address, the result is real-time measurement of carbon for each packet in and out of every data center in the world with no double counting.

Industry Collaboration

"If everyone is moving forward together, then success takes care of itself."
—Henry Ford

Collaboration has never been so important as we wrestle with the challenges of achieving net zero with a rapidly shrinking time frame to slow climate change. "Every click improves the future" is our vision. Uniting to work together as an industry is essential if we are going to make this a reality. In 2022 we are taking a major step forward as a community with the announcement of the Infrastructure Masons Climate Accord.

My fascination with sustainability started at Sun Microsystems in 2008. Like many things that Sun developed, they were ahead of their time. Sun's sustainability strategy was to achieve a balance between economics and ecology. It required an AND, not an OR. You should not have to trade off one for the other. Over the last five years, we have seen this manifest with pivots from venture, private equity, and infrastructure funds to focus primarily or even exclusively on ESG (Environmental, Social & Governance) investments. Data center expansion has never been bigger and the funding is coming from these ESG-focused firms. By coming together, we can align on how we can become the most sustainable industry in the world.

The capacity numbers I have outlined in this story are conservative. Utilization of power, cooling, space, compute, storage, and network, is lower than assumed. Bear in mind, this is not due to a lack of interest or effort. It is primarily driven by current business processes and a lack of visibility into these inefficiencies. Bottom line, there is much more stranded capacity that can be leveraged. Today I am the CEO of Virtual Power Systems, a software company focused on unlocking stranded power capacity in data centers. My team is doing our part to bring technology to the market to help our clients drive up utilization (ecology) and grow revenue without sacrificing margins (economics).

The concepts outlined in this article are meant to get the creative minds in our industry thinking about how to apply these concepts. We have multiple sessions planned with iMasons members and partners to continue the deep dive into carbon accounting and lowering the impact of Digital Infrastructure. I encourage everyone to join us! If you would like to be part of this journey of discovery, invention, and innovation, become an iMasons member at https://imasons.org/join. If you're already a member, join the sustainability group through our member platform. We would love to have you participate in our upcoming events.

---

1. Sverdlik, Yevgeniy. 2021. "Synergy Says Number of Hyperscale Data Centers Doubled since 2015." Data Center Knowledge. January 27, 2021. https://www.datacenterknowledge.com/cloud/synergy-says-number-hyperscale-data-centers-doubled-2015.

2. Kleyman, Bill. 2021. "How Digital Transformation Is Impacting Physical Modular Infrastructure." Data Center Frontier. November 2, 2021. https://datacenterfrontier.com/how-digital-transformation-is-impacting-physical-modular-infrastructure/.

3. Statista. "Number of data centers worldwide in 2015, 2017, and 2021." https://www.statista.com/statistics/500458/worldwide-datacenter-and-it-sites/.

4. https://ccaf.io/cbeci/index.

5. Statista. "Number of data centers worldwide in 2015, 2017, and 2021." https://www.statista.com/statistics/500458/worldwide-datacenter-and-it-sites/.

6. Center for Food Safety, and Applied Nutrition. 2022. "How to Understand and Use the Nutrition Facts Label." U.S. Food and Drug Administration. February 25, 2022. https://www.fda.gov/food/new-nutrition-facts-label/how-understand-and-use-nutrition-facts-label.

About the Author

DEAN NELSON

Dean Nelson is a seasoned technology executive with 32 years of experience deploying $10B of digital infrastructure projects across 3 continents. He is currently the CEO of Virtual Power Systems, a software platform that unlocks stranded power in datacenters, Founder and Chairman of Infrastructure Masons, a professional association of industry executives and technology professionals uniting builders of the digital age, and Founder and CEO of Dean Nelson Inc, a strategic advisory and consulting company serving startups, fortune 500 companies and investment firms.

Previously, Dean led Uber's Metal as a Service function supporting Uber's ridesharing business delivering over 100 million trips a week in more than 600 cities spanning 6 continents, as well as UberEats, UberFreight, UberHealth, UberForBusiness, and Autonomous vehicle and UberAir development.

Prior to Uber, Dean worked at eBay Inc as the Vice President of Global Foundation Services, which served over 300 million active users enabling over $250Bn of enabled commerce volume annually. At the end of his tenure, his team successfully integrated, then split eBay and PayPal infrastructures into two independent internet companies. Prior to eBay, Dean worked at Sun Microsystems in various technical, management and executive leadership roles.

THIRTEEN

Robert Painter

HIDDEN IN PLAIN SITE

Where are the practical efficiency solutions that are applicable to the widest range of facilities? By optimizing existing infrastructure and its operations, there are meaningful incremental improvements and efficiency gains right under your nose.

The Overwhelming Task of Energy Efficiency

Sustainability is emerging as a competitive differentiator, with a recent study citing 97 percent of data center operators claiming that at least some customers are looking for sustainable practices as terms for business.[1] However, only 43 percent say they have a strategy in place for implementing infrastructure efficiency initiatives.[2] Where to start?

When reviewing ways to make a data center more eco-friendly, a typical list might look something like this: virtualizing, consolidating, or upgrading servers; upgrading power supplies or uninterruptible power supplies (UPSs); adopting higher efficiency power voltages; and adopting new cooling systems. It may even include factors like securing a location with cooler outdoor temperatures and lower humidity, or seeking out alternative energy sources like wind or solar power. To be sure, there are many exciting and meaningful new technologies aimed at securing a more sustainable data center operation, but many of these solutions are not practical or applicable in all cases.

For starters, efficiency cannot only be about the stuff strictly used for computation, because a data center's needs vary by size and type. Smaller applications use more power for cooling equipment than for IT equipment like servers, networking, and storage. Hyperscale data centers can devote more than 80 percent of energy for IT equipment, whereas a mid-tier data center will devote closer to 50 percent.[3] Major tech companies can afford to design custom, purpose-built IT equipment, whereas a colocation facility often has no control over what IT equipment is housed in its cabinet because those choices are decided by a tenant. Drawing a distinction between IT components and infrastructure is important. After all, power usage effectiveness (PUE) ratings depend primarily on measuring non-IT based equipment: power transformers, uninterruptible power supplies, lighting, and, most notably, cooling.

More importantly, finding efficiency does not need to mean replacing legacy infrastructure by upgrading to newer, more elaborate technology. Yes, there are integrated building management systems and software solutions that monitor and automate consumption. But what about improvements to existing processes? Yes, there are terrific gains in increasing density, managing containment, and revamping floor layouts. But what about solutions that don't involve completely redesigning a facility? Yes, IT advancements have created impressive energy efficiencies (computer servers use a quarter of the energy they did 10 years ago), but aren't there efficiencies to be gained outside of a data center's IT equipment? [4] Yes, new cooling systems like direct liquid chip-based cooling or evaporative gray water closed-loops are incredible, but what about improving already-installed cooling systems?

Energy optimization should be focused on narrowing the gap between the data center's electrical load and the energy expended to power and cool it. Greener solutions don't all live outside of a data center's current setup. Often, there are significant operational savings that can be obtained through changes in operating practices rather than project-based capital investments. So, what are they, and why aren't data center organizations better at finding and executing them?

Data Center Efficiency Study: Research Design

From 2019 to 2021 a research team at Ascent conducted a study across the United States aimed at analyzing energy efficiency within the critical electrical and mechanical infrastructure of an array of data center facilities. Facilities were supported by equipment averaging 10 to 15 years of age, with an assortment of gear that was both new and ready for sunset. Each of the facilities evaluated featured approximately 60,000 square feet of total building size, with an average of 25,000 square feet of data center white space. In terms of redundancy, each had a design that would be categorized as maintainable or concurrently maintainable.

Ascent teams performed consistent assessment and data collection methodologies across all the sites. The first step was to create a complete inventory of the assets installed in support of the physical infrastructure of the building, which was primarily focused on information related to electrical and mechanical systems such as UPSs, generators, power distribution equipment, air handling equipment, and heat rejection equipment, but also secondary systems such as building controls and automation, grounding, lighting, batteries, and monitoring systems. The layout of the systems comprising the electrical topology of the sites was evaluated in detail. In addition, the Ascent teams confirmed these systems' abilities to handle critical UPS loads and the corresponding mechanical cooling loads, in addition to confirming the use of established practices for calculating PUE. The teams compared critical data center loads to the operating capacities of the corresponding electrical and mechanical infrastructure, as well as the total energy used to power at each facility during successive twelve-month periods. Beyond operational performance, efficiency was also evaluated relative to the age of the equipment.

Data Center Efficiency Study: Results and Conclusions

The overarching result of the study is that, over time, it was apparent the systems slowly fell into a state of relative inefficiency. Neither the mechanical or electrical systems in any of the facilities in this study were built with inefficiencies, nor were they designed incorrectly. However, across the board, the teams noted system inefficiencies that resulted from suboptimal initial deployments and ongoing neglect of established operational best practices.

Concerning the electrical systems specifically, there were five common areas of improvement across all the data centers under observation. First, most had no recent short circuit studies in place. Best practices support updating short circuit studies with every major equipment addition and then periodically to verify any changes to the available fault current by the utility. Next, most facilities had no recent overcurrent coordination studies on file. Overcurrent protection studies should be performed regularly to determine the appropriate breaker settings and to ensure the best possible coordination between the breakers in the power system to improve electrical reliability. Third, many simple and standard efficiency measures were missing, such as efficient LED lighting, adjustments to control systems, and the configuration of building transformers and alignment of power distribution equipment. Fourth, no site had implemented existing UPS energy savings modes, even though most of the facilities were supported by UPSs with a variety of active and passive energy-savings modes available. Activating this measure is only a matter of using existing features such as ECOMode, VMMS, or ESS. Lastly, few sites understood pertinent details of their utility contracts. While reading the fine print of a utility contract is a chore, it is important to understand the incentives and penalties included in an agreement with a provider. In many instances, the capacity of negotiated reserve power far exceeded the existing capacity of the facility. With no plans for future expansion and the confirmed ability to regain this power reservation in the future, paying for reserved capacity is unnecessary and sacrifices significant operating savings.

Similarly, there were five main findings based around the data centers' mechanical systems. To start, most sites had unmanaged supply airflow delivery losses. This can be addressed by measures such as installing blanking plates in cabinets, sealing floor openings, and installing brush-style air guards on cable cut outs. Second, most sites had supply-to-load airflow capacity losses. Another part of efficiency on the supply side is ensuring that the supply air is matched to the load. By relocating, removing, dampering, and replacing floor airflow tiles throughout the data center, only the proper amount of air is supplied to the load, cabinet by cabinet. Efficient data centers should have airflow tiles with adjustable, opposed-blade balancing dampers producing a targeted airflow of 0.05 inches of water column underfloor pressure. A third common observation was that most sites produced too much supply airflow relative to the load. When supply airflow is mismanaged, it is easy to lose sight of the fact that excess energy is being expended, much like placing a bed over a house's air conditioning ducts. Shuttering computer room air handler (CRAH) units can decrease energy consumption and provide opportunities to increase the redundancy of the air delivery system. Fourth, most sites kept their return setpoints too low and their humidity set points too high. Adjusting the return air temperature setpoints on all units to 80°F by increasing one degree per day and adjusting the humidifier control setpoints down to 30 percent relative humidity with a 37°F dew point ensures air handling units are operating within their optimal, most efficient ranges. Finally, no sites took advantage of built-in eco modes. As was the case with UPS equipment, there was a failure to enable on-board, included economizer modes. Over time, the data center community has demonstrated the reliability of these operating modes and has moved to take advantage of the cost reductions they provide as a best practice.

Based on twenty four months of post-implementation data, the results of addressing the 10 trouble spots with nominal investment were significant. For one, the properly set and coordinated electrical topology was safer and at far less risk of incident. The chance of needing to replace equipment or operate on generator power was greatly reduced. Additionally, once the improvements suggested by the study's findings were implemented and the existing electrical and mechanical systems optimized, the result was a range of 5 to 10 percent reduction in PUE. In terms of dollars, these savings netted the sites an average annual operational cost reduction of $80,000 per facility.

Why Do Data Centers Miss Low Hanging Fruit?

In sum, the greatest opportunities were found in data center operational best practices, which require that the mechanical system is delivering only what is needed to an already-optimized electrical load. The most notable aspect of the study's findings, though, is that the considerable energy savings could be achieved with such simple, low-cost solutions. All 10 areas of improvement can be considered low hanging fruit—efficiency solutions that already exist within the facility's infrastructure, waiting to be activated. So, why are data centers failing to capitalize on these easily achievable efficiencies? If these measures are layups, why are so many companies missing them? There are a few overlapping obstacles holding them back.

Overprioritization of IT Components

Even with such huge room for infrastructure efficiency improvements, energy efficiency projects often get sidelined in favor of prioritizing technological developments to keep up with the rapid pace of operational change. Or, when looking at overall energy usage, data center leaders often focus on underutilization of IT assets as the most important issue to the detriment of other aspects worthy of attention.

Risk Aversion

Implementing infrastructure changes often means a change in operational behavior. Such a change carries a perceived risk toward some impact on an application function. In such a cautious industry, uncertainty and the threat of an outage carries ramifications for the core business goal: namely reliability. As a result, energy-saving measures are often avoided for fear of downtime during its adoption.

Time Allotment

Data centers are a dynamic, complex, sometimes hectic environment where multiple parties may be accessing the same applications, servers, and platforms simultaneously, especially in the case of cloud, wholesale, and multi-tenant facilities. For some of these data centers, optimizing operations becomes a management and organizational behavior challenge—rather than a technical one—because of difficulties in handling tasks deemed to be non-urgent.

Payback Analysis

Many data center organizations use comprehensive financial evaluations to calculate the financial impact of deploying sustainability initiatives. The more complex payback analyses involve a wide array of factors, such as: asset depreciation, water usage, labor costs, maintenance and repair costs, facility age, installation time, uptime impacts, contract expenses, government or utility incentives, retraining, installation costs and the opportunity cost of lost space for larger equipment.[5] Sometimes even easily obtained gains get neglected or lost in the shuffle of such complex approval processes that leave little room for non-financial factors.

Payback analyses also cause a proclivity for more short-term thinking. Data center leaders are often wary of the immediate costs involved with efficiency measures if the perceived payback period is too long. Most data center leaders only accept payback periods of between one and five years, whereas some energy-saving initiatives take up to 15 years to cover the payback amount financially.[6] This tendency is related to the opportunity cost of not implementing a measure that may have a shorter payback period, where there is internal competition for budget items that are all viewed as a capital investment.

Staffing Constraints

Maintenance and optimization of energy-efficient technology requires an engineering staff with a degree of familiarity around the equipment. When an operational system changes, it often requires skilled staff to learn how to work with it, which can be an involved process in cases when the manufacturer offers little training or maintenance assistance. For data centers with little margin for on-the-job learning, using resources for renewed expertise is a bridge too far.

For others, staffing shortages and turnover have created knowledge gaps that either remain unfilled or lost over time, as employing the right personnel able to identify and carry out efficiency initiatives presents a challenge. In a 2021 survey by the Uptime Institute, half of those surveyed cited current troubles filling job vacancies with worthy candidates.[7] A previous study identified operations and management as the most difficult expertise type to find.[8] Some of the issues may be a result of brain drain, as other sources cite staff retention as a key worry for the industry.[9] Still others think the data center staff aging out is of primary concern, with one 2014 study estimating that 40 percent of the facilities engineering workforce is 50 years of age or older.[10] Whatever the reason, the problem may not soon be solved as the industry is set to add hundreds of thousands more positions in the next four years.[11]

A More Efficient Way Forward

There are straightforward, beneficial areas where data centers can improve their energy efficiency, but for a combination of reasons they often fail to implement them. What can data center leaders do to steer their ship in the right direction?

Adopt a Process-Based Mindset

One of the main takeaways from Ascent's efficiency study is that, to operate efficiently over time, a data center requires engineering-driven, operational best practices and vigilance—on an ongoing basis. Despite well-established best practices for lowering both PUE and water usage effectiveness (WUE) in data center facilities, inefficiency can work its way back into an efficient operation. Over time, the data center load changes and, despite best efforts, the electrical and mechanical plant begins to operate out of sync with the load. This imbalance leads to inefficiency and energy losses that can result in significant shortfalls in terms of energy dollars, as well as an increase in carbon footprint. The results of the mechanical system analysis demonstrates that the careful operation of these systems is paramount and should be monitored daily or weekly. This is because reviews of load and operating capacity, set points, and operating parameters of equipment can counteract incremental inefficiencies into the system.

For some, this process-based approach may necessitate a shift in mindset. Green data center initiatives are often ongoing, iterative activities—not one-time, set-it-and-forget-it solutions. Once an initiative has been applied to day-to-day operations then more can be added as an internal best practice. As the greener practices become further embedded into an organization's standards and protocols, the organization will become increasingly more energy conscious because power efficiency has been built into the change management process.

Combatting creeping inefficiencies may require a mindset shift in another important way as well: embracing an engineering ethos when it comes to energy conservation. Many organizations' default mode is to assume a cost efficiency ethos for energy usage by looking primarily at either carbon metrics or reduction in terms of general financial cost or operational spend. This view is essentially taking a property management standpoint, where an engineering standpoint can be more useful. By looking at the problem through an engineering lens, the problem solving takes the form of understanding the capabilities of the equipment and applying that knowledge to real-life scenarios—adjusting the variables to solve for different outputs and mitigate risk. One clear example of this mindset from the study is the savings that can come from properly assessing utility contracts to uncover hidden savings. This type of problem solving requires a methodical, engineering-based approach to validate change.

Be Knowledgeable About Your Equipment

One major cause for a lack of progress towards greater efficiency in data centers is that operators falsely assume they are already making the most of their gains with their current technology setup. To reiterate, one key takeaway from the Ascent study is that opportunities for energy savings were readily available within systems but involved education and training on energy-saving features that already existed in owned equipment. For example, energy savings modes in UPS equipment, once considered a risk, are now a reliable and economical way to recapture electrical losses in that part of the power chain. In the case of economizers or low energy modes, it is not uncommon for data centers leaders to install equipment without fully understanding what they bought —they are not aware they can simply press a button to instantly reduce their utility bill. This situation arises often in the case of turnkey projects or builds where proper education and training was not offered upon commissioning. For some legacy buildings, equipment has been functioning for a decade without anyone even trying to tweak it for efficiency.

The idea of imperfect information regarding equipment capabilities can be tied to the source of the information. Different sources—like manufacturers, governments, other industries, in-house testing, conferences, and peers—offer different qualities of information, which can affect the decision to execute a green initiative. Manufacturers' estimates on performance and energy usage, for instance, can often be unreliable because they fail to individualize based on facility factors such as facility size, location climate, or load size. The best way forward is to test and tweak equipment in-house initially, followed by operational efficiency checks at a regular interval from then on.

Putting It All Together

The path toward a greener future for data centers can appear to be dauntingly complex. However, there are many simple improvements that every data center can implement to take practical, incremental steps in the right direction. By shifting mindsets, data center leaders can overcome the barriers to realizing these initiatives in a way that sets the organization up for further success in the future.

---

1. Bizo, Daniel. 2020. "Multi-tenant Datacenters and Sustainability: Ambitions and Reality." 451 Research. September, 2020. https://go.schneider-electric.com/WW_202009_EN-Multi-Tenant-Datacenters-Sustainability-Ambitions-and-Reality-Gated-Web_EA-LP.html

2. Ibid.

3. Bullard, Nathaniel. 2019. "Energy Efficiency Is a Hot Problem for Big Tech's Data Centers." Bloomberg. December 13, 2019. https://www.bloomberg.com/opinion/newsletters/2019-12-13/energy-efficiency-a-hot-problem-for-big-tech-data-centers-k44f6m1h.

4. Knight, Will. 2020. "Data Centers Aren't Devouring the Planet's Electricity—Yet." WIRED. February 27, 2020. https://www.wired.com/story/data-centers-not-devouring-planet-electricity-yet/.

5. Klemick, Heather, Elizabeth Kopits, and Ann Wolverton. 2019. "How Do Data Centers Make Energy-Efficiency Investment Decisions? Qualitative Evidence from Focus Groups and Interviews 1." Energy Efficiency 12 (5): 1359–77. https://doi.org/10.1007/s12053-019-09782-2.

6. Ibid.

7. Ascierto, Rhonda. 2021. "The People Challenge: Global Data Center Staffing Forecast 2021-2025." Webinar, Uptime Institute, April 5 2021.

8. Ascierto, Rhonda. 2018. "Uptime Institute Global Data Center Survey."
    Uptime Institute. 2018. https://datacenter.com/wp-content/uploads/2018/
    11/2018-data-center-industry-survey.pdf.

9. Blake, Simon. 2020. "Make Data Centers Appeal To The Next Generation."
    IT Pro Portal. September 4 2020. https://www.itproportal.com/features/
    make-data-centers-appeal-to-the-next-generation/.

10. Heslin, Kevin. 2014. "Resolving the Data Center Staffing Shortage." Uptime
    Institute. August 13 2014. https://journal.uptimeinstitute.com/resolving-data-
    center-staffing-shortage/.

11. Judge, Peter. "Data Centers Need to Find 300,000 More Staff by 2025." Data
    Center Dynamics (DCD). January 28, 2021. https://www.datacenterdynamics.
    com/en/news/data-centers-need-find-300000-more-staff-2025/

About the Author

ROBERT PAINTER

Bob Painter is the President of Ascent and oversees the delivery and execution of Ascent solutions that deliver, support and complement Ascent's clients' North American mission-critical infrastructure operations. Bob leads the teams responsible for data center operations, facility management, IT site services, engineering and construction, and Navigator platform services. Additionally, he creates custom client solutions including 24×7 facility and IT services, business intelligence reporting and more.

Under his leadership, Ascent has transformed the Navigator platform to deliver transparency and insight into infrastructure data across diverse critical sites, design topologies and work management systems, including carbon emissions tracking. He fosters integrated team efforts, continual processes improvements and new technologies to ensure the Navigator platform is aligned with clients' mission-critical needs.

FOURTEEN

Avner Papouchado

5 (AND A BIT) STEPS TO GREENER DATA

"Pollution knows no boundaries any more than do money or information"
—Peter F. Drucker
Post Capitalist Society (1993)

A Context for Greener Data—What, No Elephants in the Room?

At Serverfarm, when it comes to sustainability, we don't do elephants. That is, we don't allow the big issues into the room and then keep them out of the conversation by pretending they are not there.

The time is now for an honest assessment by our collective data center sector of what we must do to provide the world with greener data. This requires a context; it means challenging some accepted truths in order to reduce, reuse, and recycle. And it calls for a change of thinking in some important areas.

The global context that will lead to the supply of greener data is the clean electrification of every industry. This requires a transition of the energy sector to net zero through complete decarbonization.

Reaching net zero by 2050 means breaking the link between all human activity and the use of hydrocarbons as fuel. It is the existential challenge of our age.

In short, everything we do as consumers and as businesses must become greener. **Furthermore**, we must also accept that where 100% green or carbon neutral is not immediately achievable, then there are vital steps to take to become green and clean wherever possible.

In data center terms, that means we must accept that changing how digital infrastructure is powered is not straightforward.

So, let's stop there for a second and ask: What is a green data center? If you are unsure, then you are not alone. It is fair to say that until recently, even within the IT industry and telecoms sectors, many people were unfamiliar with what a data center is.

What is a Green Data Center?

The data center is where the physical world meets the digital realm. A data center is a physical building that provides the space, power, cooling, and connectivity for computers to do their thing. The IT thing (also known as the workload) that happens inside the building is the storage, processing, and distribution of every type of information and data imaginable on behalf of companies, governments, organizations, and increasingly, individuals.

And we mean everything. From medical science to healthcare records, to financial statements, to utility bills, to sports statistics, to every email ever sent, to social media, to every mobile app you've ever used, or content streaming service all the way to capturing data from billions of sensors that are mapping climate change across the globe.

It is all happening in one of three types of data centers:

1. Hyperscale facilities that are mostly built, owned, and run by what has become known as Big Tech.
2. Enterprise data centers that can scale from small

computer cupboards in offices to large sites built and
paid for by banks and other big firms (unfortunately,
these are often underused and inefficient—more about
these later)

3. Commercial data centers that are run by financial and
engineering experts and in which customers locate
their IT

In sustainability terms, for each type of data center, being
green in the digital era means that what a data center is—a physical location—is now intrinsically connected with what it does,
which must involve becoming a provider of low carbon services.

As an industry, the data center sector cannot stand apart from
the people and entities that it serves.

The public profile of the data center is growing. Just as baby
boomers gave no second thought to utilities—lights came on,
water came from faucets—at the start of the ubiquitous digital
age, most people growing up in advanced economies gave no
thought to data use, data centers or clouds. Except, perhaps, when
their mobile data use hit its monthly limit.

Today consumers are becoming increasingly aware that data
has a financial and carbon cost. Just as they want energy to be
clean, they will demand that their data services are green.

Today, all digital information storage, processing, and sharing
has a carbon cost. But as the digitalization of life accelerates, and
the amount of data explodes, the associated carbon cost should
not be allowed to rise.

We often think of carbon and greenhouse gas (GHG) production as being the result of making and using physical things like
buildings, airplanes, and cars. But data centers and the services
they provide are no exception.

If we think about microprocessor manufacturing, it is clearly
raw material heavy, energy- intensive, and uses lots of water.
Turning ore into steel and cement produces vast amounts of
carbon.

Cement and steel are components of data centers. So, while

we will need new data centers, we can't simply build our way to meeting rising demand without thinking about the embodied carbon cost.

Green Data: Could all Elephants Please Exit the Building?

So, what can we do about it? Reduce, reuse, and recycle is an accepted approach to being green. Reduce means cutting the volume of resources used to achieve useful work activity. Using fewer resources means fewer raw materials for construction or avoiding new builds whenever possible.

Reuse means, wherever possible, exploring how we can make better use of and reuse existing infrastructure. It includes modernizing with the latest infrastructure for operating with less energy and water use.

Recycling should inform smart infrastructure choices. What are the raw materials? How were they produced? Can they be recycled? How can infrastructure extend the life of assets?

So, why haven't we already invented the carbon-neutral data center? To use a transportation analogy, the answer is in part that when data centers 'first came on the scene' in the late 1990s and early 2000s, everyone wanted their own car. That is, companies and organizations wanted their own standalone data centers.

Then the pooling option arrived. People got comfortable with the idea of having their data in the same building as other people's data—as long as they had access to dedicated power that was guaranteed. For them, the single most important attribute was reliability, which typically translates into a higher level of redundancy, resulting in overprovisioning and lower energy efficiency.

The next stage was the cloud. Picture a bus where everyone has enough room to travel in comfort and store all their luggage, where they get on board and alight wherever they want. That's really what the cloud is or should be.

On this special data bus, the passengers (literally packets) travel in special reserved lanes, thus getting from A to B in the fastest possible time on the shortest possible route for the lowest amount of energy. And this bus is fully fueled by green hydrogen.

Now think of a data center with those attributes. Giving people and businesses the ability to access, produce, and use ever greater amounts of data is now a net-zero game.

But for different stakeholders it does not have to be a zero-sum game. It is not a case of 'when I win, you lose.' Reducing carbon can be a win-win scenario. This is important because how a problem is viewed from the outset will determine the chances of success.

Sustainability success is Serverfarm's goal. For us, and for any business, it means taking the baggage from our metaphorical idiomatic Elephant—i.e. sustainability practicalities, transparency, accurate measurements, metrics and methods, standards and accountability—and then politely escorting it from the room.

"I think it's time we started addressing some issues around here."

Energy and Data, Some Tech Stuff About Batteries and Compressed Air and Hydrogen—*No, Really, It's Interesting and Important!*

Any success in providing "greener data" will be based on collaboration within the different sector stakeholders, between the data sector and the energy sector and with customers.

The data center industry has attracted many fine engineering minds whose ideas and progressive thinking have already led to much good work being done to tackle carbon emissions and improve efficiency.

Inside the data center sector, technological advances have the potential to help solve many of the sustainability issues in sectors like energy. There is no question that among maturing industries, data centers are the most advanced in terms of creating new approaches towards carbon neutrality.

The data center has much to teach the energy sector about technology. More broadly, data center engineering advances and the sustainability advantages of digitalization and automation that it underpins will not only address many of the challenges of climate change—it will also solve many wider societal problems. Digitalization, information, knowledge and education are fundamental to levelling up economies at differing levels of technological advancement.

"Developing countries also have the opportunity to leapfrog by adopting frontier technologies as they did when many countries skipped building a fixed line phone network and jumped immediately to mobile technology…The digital revolution provides another huge opportunity to increase the productivity of workers."[1] But we are not there yet.

What Is Happening with Green Power Inside and Around the Data Center?

Everybody talks about green data centers, but nobody knows exactly what that means. Let's explore.

As in most industries, there are many shades of green. And there are shades of green that are, in fact, closer to shades of brown. The first and the most obvious step is to improve the data center efficiency. PUE (Power Utilization Effectiveness) is the metric that quantifies the data center efficiency performance. Significant progress has been made over the years in improving the PUE from 2.0 to modern data centers operating today at 1.2, and, in some cases, even lower.

Offsetting is another tactic that data center operators have used to boost their green credentials. Offsetting is seen as a controversial method by some. Criticisms include overstating the positive impact of nature-based offsetting such as forestry projects for carbon produced today. Offsetting can also include investment in renewable energy generation. However, critics say even this does little to reduce carbon emissions at source.

More popular today are PPAs (Power Purchase Agreements). Under a PPA, companies acquire the output of a solar farm or wind farm or another renewable.

Big tech companies with hyperscale data centers to run are among the biggest investors in PPAs. The best PPAs involve direct physical connections between the renewable energy source and the data center. For this, the data center is physically located relatively close to solar or wind energy generation infrastructure so that all the energy generated goes into a grid that feeds that data center.

There are also virtual PPAs—these are more popular among data center operators. In places such as the United States, it is often easier to build a data center in, say, North Carolina and buy a wind power PPA in Iowa.

In essence, both types of PPA are closer to a real carbon reduction measure than offsetting. However, even with a physical connection, generating your own green power and feeding data centers directly is easier said than done.

It requires huge amounts of renewable generation, combined with vast storage capacity—such as batteries. In terms of a holistic view of renewables, the key is energy storage.

The available solar or wind generating capacity would need to be five times the capacity of the load required by the data center. This is because in order to be completely green, the renewable source must meet the power needs of the data center and, at the same time, charge the data center's batteries for stored energy for when the sun doesn't shine, or the wind isn't blowing.

But even battery storage with hundreds of megawatts of capacity will only run a data center for a few hours. This compares with diesel generators which are currently widely in use, which can power data centers for 80+ hours. And, of course, running diesel generators is no one's idea of green. Something must change.

Whether large energy storage systems are best at a data center or grid level (at grid level, it is known as BESS—Battery Energy Storage Systems) is being hotly debated. Wherever it lives, storage is the biggest thing that needs to be solved.

What is the cleanest technology for battery storage? Currently most batteries used in data centers are lithium-ion based. But it is likely that lithium-ion will be an interim technology for the scale of energy storage required in data centers. There is already huge amounts of research and development showing good progress in chemical batteries, flow batteries, liquid metal batteries, sodium glass batteries, and sodium-ion batteries. All of which are seen as superior to lithium-ion batteries in sustainability, performance and safety terms.

Alternative energy storage technologies that show promise include compressed air or CAES (Compressed Air Energy Storage), where the compressed air stored in underground cavities or in above-ground tanks is released to generate power using turbines, LAES (Liquid Air Energy Storage) and Pumped Hydro. Compressed air is among the most attractive solutions for data centers, and liquid air is gaining traction as a source of stored energy.

Hydrogen—Smallest Element, Biggest Hope?

Beyond using renewable energy sources – which are asynchronous and not always available—the big hope for a carbon-free fuel of the future is, of course, the simplest and the most abundant element in the universe. With an atomic structure consisting of one proton and one electron and an atomic weight of 1.008, is hydrogen the solution to carbon-free future power?

While hydrogen as a fuel will undoubtedly impact the data center industry through either fuel cells or engine re-fits, the idea of powering something like a large data center on 100% hydrogen is a long way off. The use of hydrogen will most likely come in phases:

Phase one will be the use of fuel cells or natural gas recipro-cating engines.

Phase two will be a hybrid dimension where hydrogen is injected into the natural gas pipeline at 20% - 30%, further reducing the carbon emitted from just burning natural gas. The same device, whether it is a fuel engine or fuel cell, can operate on natural gas or a mixture of natural gas and hydrogen or pure hydrogen.

Eventually, when green hydrogen becomes available, engines will be converted to run 100% hydrogen. That will be the trajec-tory of converting from natural gas.

A major factor is that to produce green hydrogen economi-cally and sustainably requires virtually free power using excess capacity from wind and solar to conduct electrolysis (separate hydrogen from oxygen in water). This is expensive because the molecular bond in H_2O is very strong and requires a lot of energy to break. And it requires a lot of electrolyzers.

A viable option is to extract the hydrogen from natural gas to capture and sequestrate the carbon dioxide produced in the reformation process.

And once all this green hydrogen becomes available, there are the problems of transport and storage. The first means building a pipeline (expensive) and the second means using compressed, liquid hydrogen, ammonia or solid hydrogen storage.

The next issue to address is how do we efficiently convert hydrogen into electricity. The conversion efficiency levels must be vastly improved from where they are today. When taking the whole cycle from renewable to end electricity, the overall efficiency is about 25% when all conversions and storage are factored in.

Instability From Stability and Back Again

There is no escaping the irony that the proliferation of renewable energy sources will have a negative impact on the reliability of the grid. If large chunks of coal or nuclear power generation are removed, this creates the need for additional "peaker" power plants that use natural gas. The solution is to have energy storage buffers that engage in these transitions.

The greener data opportunity extends to data centers playing a significant role, thereby providing this kind of storage through a demand response as well as frequency regulation, thus improving the overall grid reliability in addition to improving the data centers' own reliability.

There is much to overcome, but that should not distract nor deter our efforts.

It is important to note that on the journey to net zero, the International Energy Agency says: "In 2050, almost half the carbon reductions [will] come from technologies that are currently only at the demonstration or prototype phase."

With that in mind, here are some practical actions that data centers might consider as the first steps on the journey to greener data.

- **Step 1:** Do a PPA, whether virtual or physical
- **Step 2:** Build a microgrid with a combination of renewable power sources feeding storage devices
- **Step 3:** Eliminate diesel generators – this may not

have a major impact on carbon, but it will target
emissions
- **Step 4:** Develop designs that eliminate the use of
  water
- **Step 5:** Implement a well-established and accepted
  accounting method that would signify carbon
  reductions are real

Data About Data Centers

Because data centers house advanced IT technology, they are
often viewed as operational centers packed full of advanced technology. Sadly, for almost all, this is not the case.

Data centers are mostly operated by people walking around
with clipboards.

Nevertheless, today we are (slowly) entering an age where
automation of the data center operation is becoming a reality.
This contributes to making greener data through automating
energy provision for maximum efficiency. It is possible to ensure
electricity is supplied only to computers that are doing work and
controlling temperatures and cooling, so no waste heat is generated. Gaining insight into what is happening inside the operation
is key to running a green data center and becoming a greener data
provider. Artificial Intelligence (AI) is already used in making this
process more efficient.

Why Make More Embodied Carbon?

One step to creating greener data is thinking about building new
data centers as a plan of last resort and only where absolutely
necessary. Twenty years ago, when banks, financial institutions
and other big companies began commissioning the first generation of large data centers, they were probably unaware they would
never use them to the maximum.

During that boom, firms embarked on global data center
construction fit outs with very specific demands on design and

infrastructure resilience and location. Unfortunately, many of these facilities were never used in the way they were meant to be. Often, only less than 40% of their available capacity was used to power the data center. Much of this infrastructure is still in use today. And much of it is still underutilized and going to waste. *So, in the quest for greener data, doesn't it make sense to make use of what has already been built?*

New data center capacity requirements can be met without resorting to new buildings. The risks and costs are lower. The embodied carbon cost of new materials is avoided. The life of the existing asset is extended. Power and connectivity are already available. The infrastructure debt is turned into a sustainability credit. Power and cooling infrastructure modernization and upgrades can match the performance and efficiency of new builds.

This approach can reverse the negative impacts of infrastructure debt such as rising cost, less efficiency, and greater risk. It delivers benefits normally available only to those with the biggest requirements and the deepest pockets.

Re-use means sustainability and financial benefits are not restricted to global enterprises and hyperscale players (though they are not excluded). As a CEO of a data center operator and service provider, I speak with the big players in this industry. They are genuinely committed to their stated goals of achieving net-zero data center operations as quickly as possible. It is not a public relations exercise. It is real, and we all should understand that tackling man-made climate change through eradicating carbon and other greenhouse gas emissions is a moral and logical duty. Greener is the color for data, for business, and for the planet.

---

1.   Shafik, Minouche. 2021. *What We Owe Each Other, A New Social Contract for a Better Society*. Princeton, NJ: Princeton University Press.

About the Author

AVNER PAPOUCHADO

As the Founder and CEO of Serverfarm, with 25 years in the industry, Papouchado has been an instrumental force in the internet infrastructure market with his innovative approach to data center sustainability and growth. His formula of modernizing existing data center facilities using Serverfarm's Data Center Management as a Service (DMaaS) approach has proved to be a sustainable, economical way to meet the high capacity demands of customers. Instead of simply pushing space and power, he has been intentional about building data center solutions that get at the heart of the enterprise challenges, including automating IT management to focus on innovation, adhering to sustainability measures and level-setting balance sheets.

As Red Sea Group's North American CEO since 1993 and an active member of the executive management team responsible for the company's worldwide investment strategy, Papouchado has a proven track record of successful real estate investments. Bringing this real estate acumen together with his strategic approach in the data center sector has propelled him as a thought leader in the industry and helped enterprises accelerate their digital transformation through Serverfarm's InCommand services.

Papouchado has a B.A. in fine arts from the New School for Social Research. He is a certified pilot and avid surfer.

FIFTEEN

Michael Roark

RESHAPING THE FUTURE OF DATA CENTERS

Fire heats, wind moves, water wets, earth is solid.
Eye and sights, ear and sounds, nose and smells, tongue and tastes;
Thus with each and every thing, depending on these roots, the leaves
spread forth.
Trunk and branches share the essence; revered and common, each has
its speech.
—Shitou Xiqian

The world is big and I want to get a good look at it before it gets
dark.
—John Muir

Context (Intent)

As the founder and CEO of iM Data Centers, I am trying to
reshape digital infrastructure to embody the best in sustainable
practices: the way it's made and how it operates.

Today millions of devices, sensors, systems and applications
create a constant flow of data connected by the internet. Mobile
devices are ubiquitous, Cloud has revolutionized processing and

storing digital information, the Internet of Things is coming of age and human interaction increasingly moves online as big data continues to explode. As this speed of change accelerates, data has become our new currency to buy time, our most valuable commodity.

This groundswell of change includes five concurrent tectonic shifts in digital technology:

1. Addressing climate change with sustainable and energy efficient ways to create and operate digital infrastructure as a priority
2. The movement of big data to the 'Edge' to satisfy an exploding demand for instantly accessible, de-centralized platforms to store, analyze and transmit massive amounts of data with increasing sophistication
3. An accelerating trend for businesses and organizations to outsource IT on a subscription-based 'OPEX' model
4. The emergence of a more intelligent factory-built, modular approach to creating buildings, and
5. The energy uptick needed to support ever-increasing server requirements.

I grew up on a modest farm at the foot of the Colorado Rockies where I took every opportunity to hike and climb, and developed a deep and abiding love for the outdoors. Not able to sink my teeth into college, I dropped out, living in a small cabin at over 10,000 feet elevation for over a year and became involved with the groundswell of eastern philosophy sweeping the US during the late '60s and early '70s. I left my perch to cultivate a formal meditation practice in a monastic setting for three years. While many people my age were earning their MBAs, I was spending over six hours a day in formal, sitting meditation prac-tice, learning to empty my mind rather than fill it.

Then, still in my early twenties, I began to make my living as a carpenter and started a family. I worked my way through the trades to learn the general contracting business, then formed a construction company that grew meteorically as we built hundreds of complex projects, including high-rise buildings.

My firm started to design and build data centers in the mid-90s as well as develop multi-tenant telecom and data center properties. Fascinated by the technical landscape inherent in mission-critical facility design, we realized the immense market at hand and shifted our focus entirely to the creation of better digital infrastructure. We also created colocation data centers within our own developments, eventually creating a portfolio of facilities and a business that I sold in 2010. During the many years spent designing, engineering, building, owning and operating data centers with a tight-knit core team, we realized that data centers needed to guzzle less energy, become less expensive, quicker to make and mirror the best in environmental and corporate practices with regard to both process and product. These realizations sparked the guiding principles for a new company.

However, by that time the myriad effects of the digital age included unintended social and environmental consequences that did not align with my own values. And rather than barrel into a new wave of commerce, I felt I needed to pause and think about whether I really wanted to continue to play a small part of the creation of the infrastructure on which the digital age depends.

Thirty years ago, I perceived digital transformation and the Internet as the most powerful available tool to promote the 'democratization of information', improve quality of life, and help to level the playing field between haves and have-nots. Now seeing that it also enables an easy proliferation of myopic viewpoints that breed polarization, deepen ignorance and decrease tolerance, I experienced an existential crisis on whether to proceed. In addition to providing a great workplace, introducing energy-saving technologies and other ESG initiatives, I want my work to have deeper intrinsic humanitarian value.

During this pause, I recalled a quote by Jane Adams: *"The cure for the ills of democracy…..is more democracy"*. Expanding on this idea, from the perspective of the individual, democracy includes having a responsible share (according to one's capacity) to form and direct the activities of the groups to which one belongs, and to participate (according to need) in the group's shared values. From the standpoint of the group, it asks to actualize the potentialities of the individuals within a group in harmony with the common interests and good.

Democracy represents the possibility for individuals to participate and shape their own futures collectively in how they treat others, form new aims, and share goals to determine their mutual destinies. It is also based on a belief in the power of action informed by good faith towards the intelligent possibilities of human life and achievement.

Although the internet presumes that participants are eligible to participate in social, economic and cultural conditions that enable the free and equal practice of self-determination, the venue created to democratize information has come to include an overwhelming amount of target marketing, loss of privacy, and other dynamics that have increased the damage created by disinformation. At the same time, the internet makes censorship and centralized control difficult, promotes cultural sharing, and provides access to multiple viewpoints, equal rights and communication in all directions. While enabling disinformation with the ability to instantly transmit false reporting, conversely whistle-blowing and the ability to report wrongdoings (to prevent more) have become easier.

Technology design itself drives values, and is not just a tool to express values. For example, smartphones are also cameras with built-in apps able to instantly share personal information, easily delivered over networks that provide access across large collectives. Devices urge people to connect, express and reveal more, a value in itself. Social media enables more self-identification and ego-development by driving the creation of online identities, prompting us to codify 'what we are' to be able to communicate it. The ensuing identity reinforcement process is reinforced by the acknowledgment, approval or disapproval of the projected image by those viewing our online identities.

However, given that the digital horse already galloped out of the barn, I came around to the likely story: the solution for the ills of Internet access......is more access to more information; and then started a company to somehow address the intersection of digital infrastructure and our precious environment.

Pragmatic Steps (How)

"A master in the art of living draws no sharp distinction between work and play; labor and leisure; mind and body; education and recreation. They hardly know which is which and simply pursue their vision of excellence through whatever they are doing, and leave others to determine whether they are working or playing. To themselves, they always appear to be doing both."
—Francois Auguste De Chateaubriand

We live in a culture of wastefulness that squanders resources and engenders duplication of effort, and need to change it. Data centers guzzle phenomenally high amounts of energy: over 1% of all power utilized on a global basis (compared to the relatively tiny footprint of data center buildings) to support the irreversible trend of exponentially increasing data. Reducing the energy required to make and operate data centers lowers embodied carbon and operational carbon footprints.

The use of renewable forms of energy and resources helps sustain healthy environments we can depend upon now and in the future. Integrating conscious resourcefulness, systems thinking, enlightened engineering and ethical approaches to problem solving are now essential components of a sustainable future.

Climate change is likely the most pressing global challenge our world faces, and this challenge presents a creative opportunity to manufacture modular data centers and help decarbonize a phenomenally energy-intensive industry. The need to eliminate the depletion of natural finite resources, maintain ecological balances, conserve economic resources and promote healthy social ecosystems exists across the entire spectrum of design, engineering, processes, products and locations.

Design ideally includes carbon footprint analysis to address all systems on an integrative basis, in concert with best-in-class energy modeling solutions, and our goal is to continually seek out and improve supply chains to ensure the products and systems incorporated into data centers are responsibly made and inherently create significant energy efficiencies, thus carbon reduction.

Integrating renewable energy microgrids at data center locations, as well as placing data centers in proximity to existing renewable microgrids is well matched to the steady-state high volume power requirements of data centers.

Legacy data centers come with inherent energy efficiency challenges. For example, most data centers built during the past thirty years utilized raised flooring to provide a pressurized plenum space in which to deliver cold air upwards through perforated panels. However, it is counter-intuitive to ask cold air to rise to effectively distribute cooling for IT equipment that in some cases creates a continual oven-like heat wave. Despite the limitations of legacy data centers, there are a number of initiatives to improve sustainability, introduce renewable energy sources, reduce energy use and enlist a spectrum of other green initiatives to re-set environmental standards with no reduction of customer service.

Data centers are hardened facilities, constructed with extraordinary power, cooling and other systemic resiliency to maintain around-the-clock operations, including during disasters. Operational continuity enables a safe harbor not only for data, but also for staff and customers, reduces the need for employees to flee disaster events (such as hurricanes), and conserves and protects capital and delivers other resiliency benefits driven by uninterrupted uptime. iM Data Centers also provides a communications hotspot as a source of warning and current events information for the neighborhoods surrounding our data centers during power outages.

At iM Data Centers, we provide community engagement for the surrounding area including free website hosting for sustainability-minded groups and other organizations that support underserved, ethical goals. We develop technology incubators, engaging educational and other organizational resources to improve vocational opportunities for underserved segments of the population.

iM Data Centers carves out 5% of corporate profit to specifically promote responsible environmental causes and activism. Importantly, our key capital partner, Galway Sustainable Capital, was established solely to fund companies focused on ESG and carbon-reduction initiatives, and its principals share a deep commitment to the well-being of the environment.

Factory-Built Data Centers are the Way Forward

Factory-building data centers is inherently superior to traditional design and construction methodologies from environmental, economic and social perspectives due to the reduction of waste during fabrication processes and when operational.

Compartmentalized modular designs reduce space requirements, usage of materials, and work resources, and eliminate the need for electrical energy to support unnecessary footprints.

Modular deployments allow more flexible, conscious placement on sites to improve natural daylighting, ventilation, better water management, construction waste reduction, and other improvements towards more eco-friendly locations.

The repetitive pre-engineered solutions inherent in factory-built facilities greatly reduce conventional design and engineering processes and related costs. Predictable pricing also helps to greatly reduce typical bid and selection processes for new data centers.

Modular buildings are usually assembled and tested within the factory at the same time the related site improvements are concurrently constructed. With the ability to simultaneously manufacture and perform site improvements, modular facilities greatly reduce the long, linear design and build processes for brick-and-mortar construction. Deployment speed translates into lower finance costs and quicker turnaround. Factory-built data centers typically require structural slabs, access requirements, connections to fiber, water and power, but generally a greatly reduced amount of construction work at the site. This reduced scope of work and increased deployment speed decreases disturbance to surrounding neighborhoods including noise, pollution, traffic and other negative impacts on local environments.

Factory-building can continue irrespective of weather and other impacts that typically delay construction sites, and because modular assembly takes place indoors, production speed can be further increased by using multiple shifts.

Quality control is easier to maintain for every phase of work within a factory, particularly with workers performing predictable, repetitive tasks they've developed specialized skills for. Quality assemblies break less, require no rework and avoid many forms of material waste. Training workers to develop skills that can be used on a repetitive basis increases not only productivity but improves quality, which also reduces maintenance costs, warranty follow-up and reduces the need for repairs and replacements.

Worker safety is greatly enhanced and risk of accidents reduced by factory-building within controlled environments specifically designed and established to address potential problems. Indoor construction processes, with hoisting and fabrication technologies to assist the movement of components, assemblies and equipment within factories enhances efficiency. Manufacturing, rather than site-building, is trending toward better gender balance in an overwhelmingly male-dominated industry.

Factory-building enables more control over materials used and more conscious sourcing of materials. Consistent specification, purchasing and inventorying of green materials is easier to accomplish when buying in bulk and with organized indoor storage areas, and water damage and degradation by weather conditions are avoided. Typically, cutoffs, excess and unused materials that would normally add to local landfills close to construction sites can be stored, inventoried and used much more effectively in factory settings to minimize waste. Precise cutting of materials using repetitive computer-aided measurement eliminates work duplication and materials waste through cutting mistakes. Disciplined recycling and waste management plans along with refusing to utilize toxic components nor off-gassing materials nor other materials with those types of characteristics further reduce environmental impacts. Manufacturing allows tighter inventory processes and consistently allows more secure storage of materials and equipment, thus greatly reducing the threat of theft inherent at construction sites.

The power to cool data centers is second only to the power directly consumed by servers and other IT gear. Modular data centers can maximize Power Utilization Effectiveness (PUE), in most cases a vast improvement in comparison to traditionally-built data centers.

Increased and reliable thermal performance is achieved through an array of means, including the use of high R-value insulative materials, building skins that prevent "thermal bridging" and with "environmental locks" that can also serve as secure entry vestibules. Compact, tighter facilities are easier to cool, and the quality and precision inherent in factory-building allows better sealing and air barrier practices.

Modular buildings are inherently mobile, built to last as long as brick and mortar buildings, and can be relocated and repurposed to continue a useful life in the event they are no longer required at a particular location (in lieu of demolition which is the only option for traditional buildings that have outlived their use).

Interconnectedness (Why)

"The impalpable sustenance of me from all things at all hours of the day,
The simple, compact, well-join'd scheme, myself disintegrated,
every one disintegrated yet part of the scheme,
The similitudes of the past and those of the future...
The others that are to follow me, the ties between me and them,
The certainty of others, the life, love, sight, hearing of others."
—Walt Whitman

The shared memory of the world is now largely digital. This

digital age has enabled an everything-on-demand society, the ability to do most tasks more efficiently and quickly. It also has become easier to disconnect from the natural world around us, as the time spent and our dependence upon our devices increases. Despite this disconnect, it's also become easier to apprehend our interdependence on the world around us through the ubiquitous volume of media we ingest.

I've continued to meditate over the years. It's never seemed incongruous to wholeheartedly participate in the business world as a capitalist while dedicating part of each day to 'defragging my hard drive' (mind); reorganizing files (memories), freeing up space (unwinding) improving compute speed (creativity) and other benefits. In addition to these pragmatic enhancements, access to inner stillness (absent thought, sensation and remembrance) oddly opens a door to a 'feeling world' accompanied by a deeper sense of the interconnectedness of all life forms. And despite any differences in how we think, behave and appear, that what looks out from another's eyes is essentially no different than what looks out from yours...an awesome, mysterious sentience that we tend to take for granted.

We are connected in so many ways: by the Earth we stand upon, by the air we breathe, by the life we share, by the layers of shared ancestors from the dawn of life. Sustainability is not just a buzzword. Embracing sustainability is the only intelligent response, given the reality of our mutual predicament. It is a way to acknowledge and pay homage to our connectedness, our interdependence and whatever has sponsored this glorious pageant of life on Earth.

"To build may have to be the slow and laborious task of years. To destroy can be the thoughtless act of a single day."
—Winston Churchill

"You can observe a lot by just watching"
—Yogi Berra

About the Author

MICHAEL ROARK

Michael is a pioneer in the creation of innovative data center technologies, having built hundreds of significant mission-critical facilities in the past thirty years.

Michael founded iM Data Centers to reshape the future of data centers and address the need for increased reliance on sustainable technologies and green approaches to power-guzzling data centers using a unique modular approach: factory-building seamlessly expandable data centers with superior energy efficiency and functional intelligence at price points significantly below market. iM is also deploying a portfolio of its own data centers, utilizing its modular approach as well as acquiring traditional data centers and repositioning their carbon footprints.

Michael created numerous companies, including FiberMedia (now vXchnge), a premier provider of colocation and deep IT services and InterMetro Fiber (now South Reach Networks).

A passionate outdoorsman and advocate of sustainable practices, Michael dedicates a portion of corporate profits directly to environmental activism.

SIXTEEN

Karimulla Shaikh

AUTONOMOUS DIGITAL INFRASTRUCTURE

My Roots

My early years were spent growing up in a small town called Kandukur in India. There wasn't a whole lot for us kids to do in the town back then. One idea for fun was to chase after cycle-rickshaws that were pulled around town announcing the latest movies in local theaters. I was so fascinated by them that I was convinced life's ultimate success was to own a movie theater.

We lived near a lake that would partially dry up during hot seasons exposing dried-up clay (If you are curious, check it out at Lat/Long 15.212178, 79.905329). Our favorite hobby was to dig up this clay and bring it home to make toy replicas of cycle-rickshaws. We'd draw up mini movie-posters, stick them on these "rickshaws," and push them around the house and yard announcing the latest blockbuster releases.

Our use of clay was not limited to toy rickshaws. We made toy animals, toy houses, toy bullock-carts, and anything our young minds could imagine! My store-bought toys for the first 11 years of my life were pretty much limited to a toy steam engine and a few green plastic animal figures. I'm pretty sure that being in a situation to maximize the use of available resources helped develop my creativity and problem-solving skills.

Discovering Software

At 12, I left the small town for a big city life. The transition was difficult but was very appealing and exciting. I went on to study engineering at IIT Madras, and eventually moved to the United States to study at Carnegie Mellon University (CMU) in Pittsburgh. There were so many exciting opportunities and adventures during this period that my early life was slowly becoming a distant memory.

Immersed in technology—starting with punch card jobs for IBM mainframes and early PCs/XTs/ATs at IIT to the sophisticated computer labs at CMU, I was very busy trying to absorb the world changing around me, and me changing around the world. The world of software was turning out to be very fascinating—I could make a computer do *anything* if I could just think up the logic.

My first corporate gig was with the largest oil company in the world. I implemented a software system that created blueprints for enhanced oil recovery—which is defined as *"the extraction of crude oil from an oil field that cannot be extracted otherwise"*—after all normal extractions mechanisms have done their bit. I was already starting to make contributions to the world I would question later.

I moved to Silicon Valley to join the tech revolution just as the dot-com boom was taking off. I helped launch the first healthcare e-commerce marketplace and the first alternative to Google Translate for businesses, with a sprinkling of other startup adventures in between. The 100 miles-an-hour pace in the valley did not allow me to pause and think much about what I was doing until a mutual friend introduced me to Virtual Power Systems (VPS).

Data Center Power

When I first met Shankar Ramamurthy, the founder of VPS, in 2014, I wasn't sure how I could leverage my software experience to help him orchestrate power management in the data center. I also did not really understand what he was trying to do. What's the big deal about power in the data center? Isn't that just there when you need it? Aren't the IT servers and software applications in the data center more interesting than power infrastructure? Given my background, dealing with data center power was far from my mind.

But there was something about what VPS was gearing up to do that was intriguing. Shankar wanted to optimize power consumption to enable fully-utilized data centers. VPS was after something that Infrastructure Masons later articulated so well— "the greenest data center is one that hasn't been built." Maximizing the utilization of a data center delays the need for new data centers while still meeting growing IT demands.

As I listened to Shankar articulate how VPS is setting out to impact sustainability and the environment, something triggered in me. That lost connection I had with nature when I was young began to raise its head. Looking at everything I had focused on since then, I felt a bit guilty and somewhat ashamed. Maybe fate was giving me an opportunity to redeem myself?

It was also fascinating that VPS was doing this at the intersection of hardware and software – bringing key concepts of each world into the other. On the one hand, we were attempting to turn previously passive power hardware in the data center into an autonomous and software-controllable system that can decide how, when, and where power is delivered. On the other hand, we were trying to get software that was so used to dealing with very deterministic systems, to intelligently and autonomously orchestrate rather simple-minded power hardware. We had to keep in mind that these devices were mostly used for manual control (even if it was through a "software interface"). It was clear that we were breaking new ground in software-hardware interaction, and it was very tempting for me to want to be part of this innovation.

Green Initiatives in Data Centers

The data center industry has adopted building sustainable data centers as an important initiative over the past two decades. Nearly every DC conference has at least one track dedicated to these discussions. The adoption of Power Usage Effectiveness (PUE) as an industry metric has enabled us to measure our progress as we moved from a PUE of > 2.0 to under 1.1. This improvement in PUE represents a tremendous commitment from the industry and the tiring work of thought leaders who have innovated many ways to decrease this number with the objective of getting it as close to 1.0 as possible. For more than a decade, PUE has been the one metric that the digital infrastructure industry rallied around to slow the power consumption curve by driving efficiency in mechanical and electrical systems. However, for a truly greener data center, we must now focus on the left side of the decimal point and consider PUE of less than 1. That may sound crazy, but it *is* possible if we can identify and leverage the stranded power capacity that goes completely unused in the data center.

Stranded Capacity

In most data centers, power infrastructure is underutilized for three common reasons:

- **Redundancy** - Data centers have at least 20% of redundant capacity built into the infrastructure to account for potential failures - this can be as high as 100% for 2N data centers
- **Allocation Buffers** - Colos and facilities teams give themselves a buffer as a "just-in-case" on top of contracted capacity

- **Underutilization** - Despite what their contracts might say, tenants often underutilize their contracted capacity the majority of the time (> 99%); their contracts are usually negotiated for worst-case scenarios

When you combine these three reasons, there can be more than 60% of power capacity that is not utilized. To get an idea of what this means in the real world, Infrastructure Masons has reported that up to 37GW of capacity is not utilized[1]—and that calculation was only one portion of the stranded power-underutilization. If you add redundancy and buffers, we might be getting to more than 50GW of capacity that has been built but not utilized. If we can deploy additional IT capacity to use all this stranded capacity, it mitigates the need to prematurely build new data centers and thus can contribute to the idea of the "greenest data center". This is the new approach that can optimize what we have built versus perpetuating the underutilization that is prevalent in the digital infrastructure industry.

However, stranded power capacity exists for a reason—to mitigate potential failures and to reduce the impact of unexpected changes in utilization. How do we then recoup this stranded capacity while still being cautious about these potential risks?

Virtualization as a Direction

For this, we draw an analogy with how VMWare revolutionized computing in the early 2000s. Compute virtualization pools CPUs and allows system administrators to create multiple smaller virtual machines on the servers sharing the CPUs and running independently of each other. These virtual machines can be started and stopped as needed, depending on the workload requirements of an organization or schedule. A virtual machine can also be moved to another server if its current host server is already maximized by active virtual machines.

This flexibility allowed IT administrators to create and orchestrate virtual machines in a way to ensure maximum utilization of CPUs for most of the time. In essence, they were able to recoup the stranded compute capacity as new capacity on which more virtual machines could be instantiated. The concept of Virtualization has now evolved to sophisticated offerings with cloud-service provider (CSP) offerings such as AWS's Elastic Compute Cloud (EC2), Google Cloud Platform's Google Compute Engine (GCE) and Kubernetes container orchestration.

All these platforms strive to provide customized offerings tailored to leverage the building blocks of SDC (Software-Defined Compute) to the needs of customers. For example, AWS EC2 offers different instance types optimized for compute, memory or storage (or a general purpose instance type if you can't make up your mind). It also offers different payment plans such as on-demand, reserved, or spot instances so you can pay exactly for what you intend to use.

Before these offerings, IT administrators were used to buying or leasing servers and committing to them for multiple years. Now, they can take advantage of these options to perfectly right-size their server provisioning and pay only for what they actually need or use.

Why did I spend so much time discussing VMware and compute virtualization? This innovation paved the way for other virtualizations such as Software-Defined Networking (which helped separate the physical network from the control plane) and Software-Defined Storage (which separated management of storage from the hardware layer). We can now extend this to data center power management through the concept of Software-Defined Power (SDP). SDP uses a similar approach to virtualize the power control plane separating it from power infrastructure and unlocking the stranded power for more IT capacity.

Software-Defined Power

With Software-Defined Power, we virtualize the power infrastructure and treat it as a pool of power capacity. The analogy to virtual machines is pools of power where each pool is dedicated to work-loads with a given availability requirement. Just as computer virtual-ization chunks CPUs into smaller virtual blocks and allocates them to virtual machines, we chunk breaker capacity into smaller chunks of power that can be allocated to different pools at different times. The power allocation is dynamic and is based on the actual consumption requirements of a given pool of workloads at any time.

A software orchestration system coordinates power availability using intelligent power switches and local energy storage located north of each pool of power. Depending on the current and predicted power consumption patterns, the software orchestrates the intelligent switches to turn power on or off based on SLA requirements of individual pools. To mitigate risks, the orchestra-tion includes mechanisms to notify IT owners before any changes to their workloads, so that they can proactively do a soft shutdown.

With the ability to create SLA-driven pools of power, the facil-ities and IT teams (or colos and tenants) can work together to deploy a mix of critical and non-critical workloads to the full capacity of the data center. If existing tenants do not have a need for non-critical workloads, colos can sell lower SLA pools to new tenants at an attractive pricing.

New Product Offerings

Traditionally, data centers have sold capacity to tenants as a single SLA, which is generally five 9's. Going back to our discussion on stranded capacity, data centers use redundancy and buffers to ensure they can make this capacity available to their tenants. The tenants themselves sign up for the highest utilization expected (with their own buffer, of course) which means the utilization is far below the contracted capacity for the majority of the time.

It's time for data center operators to learn from how AWS and GCP were able to leverage virtualization to offer right-sized prod-ucts for their customers through on-demand, reserved, and spot instances. Colo operators can similarly create new SLA offerings that allow tenants to commit to a lower capacity and purchase the option of spiking to a higher utilization only when needed. They'll only need to pay for the higher utilization when there is a need (à la spot instances).

Colo operators can also offer appropriate products to new tenants seeking non-critical SLAs at lower cost. These tenants previously could not afford the one-size-fits-all offering available to them. By appropriately signing up a mixture of tenants with different SLA pools, colo operators can increase their revenue significantly without having to make large investments.

Data centers have to work hard to create and maintain a market distinction in the industry. Innovative efforts such as a more efficient cooling delivery system to reduce the PUE help stand out in the market, but it comes with a significant investment. New product offerings with Software-Defined Power bring this market distinction at a fraction of the cost and are truly innovative because they bring visible and direct cost-savings to tenants. This also increases the yield of capital investments as capacity utilization can increase dramatically, delaying the need to build more infrastructure. In essence, data centers get more out of what they build.

All this sounds great, but just how does software really enable these differentiators and new product offerings?

Autonomous Digital Infrastructure

Since software is a key player in this scenario, let's examine a few roles it fulfills, especially making this an autonomous system. We can view this entire ecosystem as an Autonomous Digital Infrastructure (ADI).

First, the software needs to monitor and assess the data center to identify opportunities to create new pools and product offerings. This involves a complete analysis of redundancy, buffers and utilization to determine how much power is stranded, where it is stranded, and how much of it may be recouped for new IT capacity.

Second, the software needs to make recommendations on new product offerings and provide a comprehensive risk assessment to the colo operator. Given the typical stranded power in the data center, a good portion of the stranded capacity can be turned into new pools of power with little or no risk.

Finally, once the pools are defined and as tenants come on board, the software needs to monitor utilization of each pool to determine if an action is needed and execute the appropriate action autonomously.

This decision-making logic needs to consider a number of factors. It needs to account for expected power consumption patterns, which can be derived from the current instantaneous power consumption, historical power consumption behaviors, and seasonal variations (which could be hourly, daily, weekly, monthly or annual). It needs to account for Artificial Intelligence and/or machine learning models that can assess these factors on historical data and can help make these predictions. It needs to account for the SLAs associated with each pool and consider any prior impacts on the pools due to previous decisions. This ensures that we are operating the pools within their required SLAs.

As a useful extension, the orchestration can take advantage of instrumentation built into modern-day workloads running on the IT equipment. This instrumentation often allows the workloads to manage their own capacity, either by reducing the number of instances or by redirecting workloads to alternate locations through load balancing. In these cases, the ADI software can proactively communicate with application software agents to control the workloads before resorting to activating the physical intelligent switches.

Providing such a mutual interface between the ADI software that is managing the facility power and the application software agents which can manage the workloads allows the two worlds to set and manage expectations with each other autonomously. The truth is, this is just the beginning of what's possible with Software-Defined Power.

ADI Policies and the Role of Hardware

While ADI software will be able to control the power hardware available in the market today, a big opportunity awaits for innovation in the world of power hardware to make it even more suitable for automation. We can introduce policies for communication of decisions between the two systems. The ADI software generates and pushes these decision-making policies to the devices. The policies provide the device with a variety of choices based on the current status of the data center, and the devices are allowed to choose an option based on the local state in the proximity of the device. A big advantage of such a policy is that the device can make an immediate decision based on the local state without waiting for a final decision to come from a central software. These policies could be updated periodically based on the changing nature of the data center.

Using such policies gives us two advantages. First, the device can respond quickly to state changes and eliminate risks of delay. This ability to respond in real-time allows the data center to recoup more of the stranded power as new pools. Second, the ADI software can provide time-varying policies based on predicted power patterns in the data center. Such policies can be valid for as long as 24 hours or more.

These types of policies push more intelligence to the edge devices and make the ADI software more of a strategic decision-maker. This allows for the data center infrastructure to make autonomous, yet coordinated, decisions even when the software is not actively communicating with them. The idea of using policies is not new in the industry. Some of these concepts are already being applied on the grid-side wherein systems are capable of automatically responding to demand-response events from the utility provider through a set of policies to shed loads as needed.

It's time to bring this policy-driven control inside the data center as well.

By making a majority of these decisions autonomous, data center operators avoid having to manually react to day-to-day issues and can focus on making strategic decisions that drive the autonomous infrastructure. Their focus is now on deciding how much of the stranded power is to be recouped, how many new product options are to be offered, and how to configure these on the software for autonomous control. By automating a lot of the daily activities, we can also eliminate potential human errors, something that has historically been responsible for the majority of data center failures that caused downtime.

Well, are we there yet?

Path to ADI

It took computer virtualization ten years to take hold in production environments. We expect it to be not that different for power virtualization. At VPS, we have been working to bring this to the mainstream for over eight years, and this idea is now being accepted as a key differentiator by data center operators. Power equipment vendors have also taken notice. While initially viewed as competition, it has now become clear to them that Software-Defined Power is the future of the industry, and it's important to make it a key segment in their portfolio. Many vendors are exploring how to make their power equipment SDP compatible. Incidentally, this collaboration is also elevating the security and state-of-the-art expectations on the embedded software and controllers in these devices. Given the heightened awareness of infrastructure security, this can only be good news for all of us!

Takeaways

Software-Defined Power with ADI brings market innovation, competitive advantage, and right-sized product offerings to the industry. Over the last seven years, as I delved deeper into this world with customers, partners, vendors, collaborators and colleagues, a few things have become very clear.

First, what we have is a disruptive concept in the data center: elevating human control to a strategic level and leaving the day-to-day decisions to an automated system. This is a difficult thought in a traditionally conservative industry. I encourage readers to review other virtualization examples and how they have become tremendously successful in previously conservative industries as well.

Second, as we discussed, there is a need to rethink the SLA offerings between colos and tenants (or, in an enterprise data center—the SLAs between IT and facilities) to get the most out of the data center's power infrastructure. This again requires us to change the way we have done business for a long time. Consider the example of McDonald's franchise owner Jim Delligati's experiment in 1972.[2] He started selling donuts and sweets during breakfast hours at a Pittsburgh restaurant which eventually led to a full breakfast offering in 1977. That turned into 25% of McDonald's revenue providing a massive boost to their global business. McDonald's did not know at the time that customers wanted more meal choices. In comparison, data centers today offer one five-course meal manifesting as a 5-9 or greater SLA. As cloud has shown, one size does not fit all. It's time we start expanding our menu to match the demand of data center customers.

Here's what you can do:

- If you are a data center operator, engage with the tenants and help them rethink how they do their contracts so they can right-size them, save themselves money, and give you additional capacity to sell a second time.
- If you are a colo tenant, ask your colo operator how you can avoid paying for capacity you rarely use, save money in the process and still have access to that capacity when you do need it.
- If you are a vendor, get ahead of the curve by building SDP concepts into your hardware offerings.

- If you are a data center designer, start baking these concepts into your designs today so you can future-proof your data centers and make them SDP-compatible.

It's time for our industry to maximize power utilization with Autonomous Digital Infrastructure and Software-defined Power. We need to not build that data center we don't need, while turning what we have into a sustainable one. This is key to our vision of greener data. My most recent journey felt a bit like molding clay cycle-rickshaws with muddy hands again. It wasn't just creative and fun, it was also natural and fulfilling—a connection back with Planet Earth, perhaps? Apparently, I just needed to think like a kid again, and I invite you to do the same.

---

1. Nelson, Dean. 2022. "Defining The Digital Infrastructure Industry." Inter-Globix Magazine. February 10, 2022. https://www.interglobixmagazine.com/defining-the-digital-infrastructure-industry.
2. Daszkowski, Don. 2020. "The Facts on Where Fast Food Breakfast Got Its Start." The Balance Small Business. January 3, 2020. https://www.thebalancesmb.com/history-of-fast-food-breakfast-1350969.

About the Author

KARIMULLA SHAIKH

Karim is Chief Technology Officer at Virtual Power Systems (VPS), where he drives the company's innovative Software-Defined Power products that enable data centers to achieve savings and sustainability through automation and power orchestration at the intersection of hardware and software.

A technologist with a passion for bold and critical thinking, Karim is also on the faculty at Carnegie Mellon University's Integrated Innovation Institute, where he teaches machine learning, software architecture, design thinking and futures studies, empowering his students to take a futures-based approach to product development.

Karim is a seasoned executive with over 25 years of product management and software engineering experience at both early-stage startups and established enterprises. Prior to VPS, he was Senior Vice President of Product Development at SDL Language Technologies, a global leader providing language translation software to Fortune 100 companies.

While he enjoys getting into the technical guts of scalable and reliable cloud software products, Karim is equally enthusiastic about building high-performance teams by transforming people and process interactions.

SEVENTEEN

Braham Singh

PAVING THE PATH AHEAD: THE BRIGHT, THE BOLD, THE CONTROVERSY

It's no secret that sustainability is a global emergency. As each year passes by, the climate crisis intensifies, and so does the need to reduce the carbon footprint of enterprises and, by all accounts, data centers. Becoming sustainable is more than a corporate initiative or Earth Day pledge. More needs to be done. Actions need to be taken. Greenwashing needs to end. The infrastructure community united can truly make a difference. More public-private partnerships need to be formed across sectors so that together we stand a better chance at leaving the world a better place for our children and grandchildren.

While the future is filled with plans to tackle the sustainability emergency, there are still so many obstacles to navigate, especially when it comes to the hotly debated carbon credit industry. In a recent Impakter Magazine editor's pick article,[1] I pointed out that analysts predict offset purchases could be more than $50 billion by 2030, if not sooner.[2] But how much is really being offset?

It's a controversial topic, I know. And one that I plan to write my own book on someday, a forum where I can dive into what I call the *Cop Out at COP26* and dissect this topic even further. But one point that I feel strongly about is that there's still no robust tracking mechanism in place post-COP26 to pre-empt reselling a credit already sold. I'm sure many would agree that it's mind-blowing, but here in this chapter, I will speak of solutions and the steps that I and the company that I lead, BDx, are taking to ensure carbon credits are being tracked accurately across our footprint and beyond.

A Look on the Bright Side

Before diving into ways to ensure accurate tracking of carbon credits, let's take a stroll down the bright side. Billions are dropped annually into initiatives and solutions to help mitigate this sustainability crisis, along with enormous worldwide efforts to hit aggressive net-zero targets. In fact, according to UN.org, more than 70 countries, including the biggest polluters—China, the United States, and the European Union—have set a net-zero target, covering about 76% of global emissions.[3] Over 1,200 companies have put in place science-based targets in line with net-zero.[4] More than 1000 cities, over 1000 educational institutions, and over 400 financial institutions have joined the Race to Zero,[5] pledging to take rigorous, immediate action to halve global emissions by 2030.[6]

The evolution of technology has indeed created groundbreaking ways to empower a more sustainable future—and we (as an industry) have come a long way. In some respects, the world is lucky enough that today's carbon-related calamity comes at a time when technology is at its peak, when corporations and governments are standing together to fight climate change, and when data centers and cloud providers are enabling digital transformation and making their own pledges to increase efficiency, digitally transform, and reduce carbon emissions.

The road ahead can be vibrant, especially when it comes to decarbonization, carbon counting and tracking, managing infrastructure, and maximizing capacity to optimize efficiency. But we have some work to do, and time is of the essence.

The Next Wave of Sustainable Data Centers From the Asia-Pacific

This next era of green data centers and management is at the heart of BDx; it is the core of our vision and mission, etched in our DNA. As innovators across the Asia-Pacific, where we live, work, and are expanding the BDx footprint, we look to adopt better solutions and forge meaningful partnerships to solidify a more sustainable future. As a young organization, we realize that we have the opportunity to push our initiatives forward from the jump so that as we continue to grow, we grow greener and more deeply intertwined into emerging markets that also strive to be more sustainable.

In Singapore where BDx operates a data center and where we recently relocated our global headquarters, we've invested in a long-standing partnership with two highly regarded entities. This partnership was formed in late 2021 with The National University of Singapore's Faculty of Engineering (NUS Engineering) and Sembcorp Marine to explore the development of underwater data centers. Through such a meaningful public-private relationship, all parties involved also seek to address the overall growing climate and sustainability challenges facing the data center industry and environment.

Under a Memorandum of Understanding (MOU), each party in this alliance will contribute a unique element to advance the development of sustainable ocean data centers:

- BDx will provide the data center arrangement as well as the technical proposal and operational strategy.
- NUS Engineering will supply its cooling technology along with metrics for meeting relevant energy efficiency targets.
- Sembcorp Marine will contribute an offshore platform solution.

Alliances such as this one that we're building in Singapore—a key global hub not just for data centers—are a prime example of how a united data center industry, in particular, is more equipped to fight on the frontlines to build a better, more sustainable tomorrow. However, partnerships along these lines are blossoming across industries, and rightfully so. Alone, organizations can only go so far. Together, they can conquer and build for our next generation, their children, and for epochs to come.

The Mighty Lion City Lifts Moratorium

If we take a closer look at the headlines coming out of Singapore, it's evident that sustainability is at the forefront. Even though the island city lifted its temporary moratorium on new data center builds, it will be more selective of data center investments moving forward. Particularly, according to Singapore's Minister for Trade and Industry Gan Kim Yong, this digitally-focused hub seeks to "anchor data centers that are best in class in terms of resource efficiency, which can contribute towards Singapore's economic and strategic objectives."[7]

Data centers are driving the digital-first community in the mighty Lion City but must look to innovation and new ways to build data centers and generate power. The 70 data centers in this leading data center hub generate around 14,000 MW of capacity, and that number will only continue to grow because Singapore is as courageous as it is loud when it comes to technology and innovation. And digital-first environments need data centers, plain and simple.

Part of the reason BDx packed up our global HQ and moved to Singapore is to be a part of the solution and work diligently and hands-on with public entities to explore alternate ways to continue innovation and smart initiatives. At the same time, it's critical to work towards building a more sustainable model in Singapore that can be applied to new and emerging markets.

The Transformation of DCIM: Meet 360°View

Another order of business BDx tackled to push our sustainability agenda ahead is the transformation of traditional DCIM (Data Center Infrastructure Management) across our facilities and beyond. Our innovation department knew DCIM-type solutions aren't robust enough. DCIM wasn't created for one of the biggest battles of our lifetime; its limitations don't allow it to track carbon credits. It's aged. So, after coming to the conclusion that DCIM was inefficient, lagged in technology, and could no longer meet the vital needs of sustainable enterprises—not only those colocating across our BDx data centers but everywhere in the world—we adopted a new platform to transform data center management, increase sustainability and accurately track carbon credits. ***Enter 360°View.***

At BDx, we think of 360°View as the worst enemy of DCIM and the carbon accounting industry. That may sound a little harsh, but the reality is that a platform on this level is really going to shake things up. That's why we are committed to it, believe in its capabilities, and have been deploying it for our customers and across our own data centers for over three years.

To define it in words doesn't do it much justice; its true definition lies in its results. But at a high level, 360°View is a hybrid infrastructure management platform for managing mission-critical infrastructure whether in your data center, in a colocation facility, or in the cloud. It provides intelligent and predictive management of capacity, power, and assets to enable a more sustainable future. It is cloud-based and leverages blockchain technology. The latest iteration of 360°View measures and reduces an organization's carbon footprint and is vendor and data center agnostic. The platform delivers in-depth insights and visibility anywhere, anytime, and from any device.

Transparency in Tracking Carbon Credits

See, in my opinion, the carbon credit industry is flawed. It's just not accurate. It's not making enough of a difference. It's a multi-billion-dollar industry. And while carbon credits and offsets are necessary, the way they are tracked and accounted for must be refined. Here's where 360°View really steps up to the plate to deliver.

The 360°View experience offers comprehensive features, including connecting to carbon registries and carbon credit token blockchains. While I could go on about the multitude of benefits 360°View provides to save enterprises millions and become more sustainable, here's a snapshot of its most significant additional features:

- Colocation and total power management
- A unified physical security command center
- Automated and integrated workflow management
- Asset performance and lifecycle management
- Sustainability trackers, including accurate measurement of PUE (Power Usage Efficiency), CUE (Carbon Usage Effectiveness), and CoP (Coefficient of Performance)

This innovative platform was developed to eliminate the complexity associated with carbon accounting and tracking carbon credits or offsets. The various carbon exchanges and bodies administering carbon credits and Renewable Energy Certificates (RECs) currently rely on third-party consultants to validate credit and offset claims. This human factor is cumbersome, expensive, and prone to conflicts of interest. It is also known to be error-ridden, and double counting is a significant problem. As Greenhouse Gas (GHG) producers pledge to reduce their carbon footprint and commit to aggressive net-zero or even carbon-negative goals, 360°View provides them with a solution to track and measure carbon accurately 24x7x365 with zero human intervention. On the back end, 360°View can either digitally submit applications to traditional carbon exchanges or become a trusted node in any carbon token blockchain.

Data Center Digital Transformation

Our movement has only just begun as we push forward with our native green philosophy and sustainability action plans to make a difference across Asia-Pacific and truly the world. There's so much still to accomplish, and we hope to achieve all that we have set out to do. I know we're small fish in a big sea, but that really doesn't matter. What matters is we work hard to achieve our goals and put passion into action.

In Singapore, BDx brings a unique perspective with our exploration of modern ocean data centers. In China, our Nanjing facility was built to rigorous specifications to meet sustainability requirements, and in Hong Kong, we continue to modernize our facilities to increase efficiencies across all facets.

We are also empowering more efficient and sustainable data centers through an agreement with Red Dot Analytics (RDA)[8] to transform BDx's facilities digitally. The first phase of a three-year project with RDA, a Singapore-based pioneer in the industrial artificial intelligence (AI) space, will focus on cooling and PUE optimization at our facilities in mainland China, Hong Kong, and Singapore.

This type of agreement enables our operational teams to identify inefficiencies throughout its facilities by leveraging RDA's Data Center Solution that integrates AI-driven applications and automation. As a result, operations will gain deep insight into data center lifecycle management while delivering lower energy costs, less human error, and increased capacity utilization. Ultimately, this will help us reduce our carbon emissions and footprint, which is critical as the demand for digital continues to increase the need for data centers.

Peaceful Disruption

With all of the peaceful protests in the world, you would think there would be more meaningful demonstrations around climate change. I mean, that's not to underrate the purpose or critical importance of other protests, just that the climate crisis is just as, if not more, vital. More leaders, corporations, and individuals need to stand up for what they believe and act on it. This brings me back to my earlier point around what a Cop Out COP26 was.

A few years ago, I came across a story[9] about an environmentalist who proposed turning Earth Day into a protest of sorts that aimed to hit the biggest contributor to our environmental crisis, the fossil fuel industry. She planned to initiate a "non-idling" day on Earth Day. The goal was to send a wake-up call to the fossil fuel industry and prove that our small sacrifices actually prompt governments and decision-makers to take the larger actions needed to save the planet. I commend this kind of peaceful protest. And in some ways, I hope through solutions such as 360°View, we send a wake-up call to the carbon tracking industry.

See, sometimes it's the small actions that will lead to real change. Enough of them will make a difference. So, no matter how small you think your ideas are to join in on this fight, bring them on. 360°View may not change the world, but it's a small step in the right direction to boost sustainability and uncover the carbon credit industry's insufficient ways of tracking.

Leaders of the infrastructure community are working hard to make a difference and turn this catastrophe around. I'm committed to helping lead this fight, and I invite others to join me and the BDx movement towards green data centers. I often participate in sustainability-focused forums and panels in Asia-Pacific and the U.S. to learn from others and expand my knowledge. We're a critical yet small industry, and we must continue to develop our wisdom and lend our insights to make an impact, no matter how small.

1. Singh, Braham. 2022. "Unfettered Carbon: Why Blockchaining Is Essential but Not Enough." Impakter. February 16, 2022. https://impakter.com/unfettered-carbon-credits-why-blockchaining-is-essential-but-not-enough/.
2. Taskforce on Scaling Voluntary Carbon Markets. 2021. "Summary Packet." Institute of International Finance.. January 25, 2021. https://www.iif.com/Portals/1/Files/TSVCM_Summary.pdf.
3. UN Environment Programme. 2022. "Addendum to the Emissions Gap Report 2021: A preliminary assessment of the impact of new or updated nationally determined contributions, other 2030 pledges and net-zero emissions pledges announced or submitted since the cut-off dates of the Emissions Gap Report 2021." UN Environment Programme. https://wedocs.unep.org/bitstream/handle/20.500.11822/37350/AddEGR21.pdf.
4. United Nations Global Compact. 2022. "Business Leaders Taking Action." UN Global Compact. March 3, 2022. https://www.unglobalcompact.org/take-action/events/climate-action-summit-2019/business-ambition/business-leaders-taking-action.
5. United Nations Framework Convention on Climate Change. "Race to Zero." 2021. UNFCCC. April 23, 2021.https://racetozero.unfccc.int/join-the-race/.
6. United Nations, Net Zero Coalition. https://www.un.org/en/climatechange/net-zero-coalition.
7. Ministry of Trade and Industry Singapore. 2022. "Written reply to PQ on data centres." Ministry of Trade and Industry Singapore. January 11, 2022. https://www.mti.gov.sg/Newsroom/Parliamentary-Replies/2022/01/Written-reply-to-PQ-on-data-centres.
8. https://www.rda.ai/.
9. Hausmann, Gisela. 2020. "A Call for Earth Day 2020: Make it a No-Idling Day." Impakter. January 1, 2020. https://impakter.com/call-for-earth-day-2020-no-idling-day/.

About the Author

BRAHAM SINGH

With more than 30 years of experience in the telecom industry, Braham Singh has been instrumental in the founding and strategic development of Big Data Exchange (BDx). As CEO of BDx, Singh has led the development of Asia-Pacific's premier data center, colocation, and hybrid cloud solutions provider. Singh's knowledge of data centers, content delivery networks, and cloud services across global markets has helped him grow BDx's customized suite of offerings.

Prior to joining BDx, Singh served as IDC & Associated Business CEO, where he worked with HGC to develop BDx. Singh was senior vice president for Global Product Management of Reliance Communications & Global Cloud Xchange. He was also the CEO of Red Snapper, a Malaysian government-funded initiative to promote the growth of wireless broadband in the country. Prior to that, he was employee #1 at PCCW owned BTN, which grew under him to become PCCW Global.

EIGHTEEN

Wes Swenson

IT'S NOT EASY BEING GREEN: DATA CENTERS AND HOLISTIC ENVIRONMENT SUSTAINABILITY

A child of the 1970s and '80s, I grew up with a certain perspective on our environment, though we didn't call it environmentalism, and sustainability wasn't a part of our vocabulary. Neither was the idea of being "green." I more readily associated green with Kermit the Frog from The Muppets when he sang, "It's Not Easy Being Green," likewise, an appropriate title for today's green-conscious world. Whereas Kermit's song was about an acceptance of his unchangeable green color, today we aspire toward a much-idealized green environment. But as we see in the world, *aspiring* to be green is harder than *actually* being green.

Regardless of the terminology we used; conservation, environ-mentalism, and sustainability have been part of our collective consciousness for at least the last 50 years and maybe longer. The first Earth Day was celebrated in 1970 with locally-organized gatherings, and a year later on Earth Day 1971, a Keep America Beautiful advertisement gave Americans a memorable slogan urging them to act: "People start pollution. People can stop it." I can also still recall the words of Woodsy Owl in PSA campaigns: "Give a hoot, don't pollute," and "Help keep America looking good." Growing up in Utah, the often-taught curriculum in elementary school was "slow the flow" or "stop the drip," to combat water waste and droughts. I grew up in an age where battling chlorofluorocarbons for the sake of the ozone was a central theme; and air pollution, plastic production, and toxic waste presented additional challenges to an increasingly consumeristic world.

But who knew what the future would hold, and how important this topic and our society's moral obligation to "be green" would become? I believe many of us felt inclined toward conservationist initiatives and we tried to act accordingly, but looking back, there can be little doubt that we lacked a sense of urgency, even as we were flooded with messages inspiring us to pay attention to the environment. Unfortunately, corporations and consumers either didn't anticipate the impact, dismissed it out of hand, or worse yet, only did what they had to until either the government dictated it, or consumers demanded it. What we lacked then was a focus on holistic environmental sustainability and a centralized vision for fixing the overall impacts we were having on the environment.

Fast forward to today, and our technology-driven world has accelerated the impacts our society has on the environment in ways that Woodsy Owl and my teachers in Utah couldn't have predicted. As someone who has been in the technology business since the mid-1980s, I've seen many of these impacts firsthand. My career ranged from semiconductors to desktop and security software until data centers emerged as my chosen industry in 2007. The easiest way to delve into data centers' environmental impact is by starting with an examination of what led to their prominence: the internet.

The Emergence of Data Centers and Their Environmental Impacts

The internet sprang from two computers communicating at an MIT Lincoln Lab in 1965, and the first Internet Service Provider (ISP) was born in 1974, which was a commercial version of ARPANET, known as Telenet. In 1991, CERN, the European

Organization for Nuclear Research introduced the World Wide Web to the public. For the most part, the World Wide Web, or what we now call the internet, has been with us since 1991. According to the International Telecommunication Union, a United Nations agency that reports on information and communication technologies, the number of internet users worldwide has increased five-fold since 2005, growing from 1 billion users then to more than 4.9 billion internet users in 2021.[1] The majority of that internet traffic is routed through data centers.

Data centers took root in what we called server closets—which were literal closets built to house the extremely hot and noisy gear required to accommodate internet traffic and data storage. As the internet grew, so did the placement of mini-mainframes and servers. Server closets transitioned to dedicated rooms and offices before occupying building floors, and eventually, entire buildings. Now we see them as campuses and massive hyperscale facilities eclipsing 100 acres and millions of square feet of space.

With increasing size, increasing environmental impacts have followed. According to the International Energy Agency, data centers accounted for 1% of global electricity demand in 2020.[2] Considering that global internet traffic continues to grow, with a reported near tripling of bandwidth between 2017 and 2021, the data center industry will continue expanding exponentially to keep pace, with no end in sight for the foreseeable future.[3]

So, how can we become better stewards of our local, national, and global environments as it concerns data centers? I believe in a holistic approach that covers such major items as the sourcing of our energy to minor things such as refillable water bottles. Waterless cooling and renewable energy are other big pieces of the pie. It is not just one consideration, but a cultural shift in reducing our impact on the environment to improve the quality of our lives and the lives of those who come after us. Future technologies will change and allow us even more opportunity to adapt and reduce our impact. Additionally, inculturating green consciousness requires agility that considers regional geographies, economies, and resources. Above all, we should always seek improvement and never allow the designs and builds of the prior decade to stagnate and lure us into false security and comfort.

Keeping environmental impacts in mind are what urged me to do things differently when I started my company Novva Data Centers. Down to the smallest detail, our facilities are designed with innovation and sustainability in mind. Nowhere is this commitment more evident than on Novva's 100-acre campus in Utah, featuring 1.5 million square feet of technologically advanced data center space equipped with top-of-the-line sustainable features, including almost three feet of insulation, waterless cooling, use of renewable energy and hot air containment. Our flagship LEED-certified facility opened in September 2021 and demonstrates what's achievable when data center operators focus on going green.

Based on my experience, I'd like to offer a few observations on how data centers can reduce their impact to the environment and improve the sustainability of the resources we consume both immediately and long term.

Considerations for Reducing the Environmental Impacts of Data Centers

Site Selection

Data center location is one of the most important factors as it relates to carbon emissions and environmental impact.

We need to keep in mind that there are two sources of primary energy draw for data centers. The first is the energy required to power battery systems that supply the energy to the servers. Second is the energy required for cooling to allow the servers to operate at optimum efficiency. Depending on the environmental impact you are focused on, different climates provide advantages. As an example, hot desert environments are less desirable than high altitude cold environments when it comes to cooling your data center. Deserts have fewer hours that data centers can use ambient air (or free cooling). They must generate cool air either through refrigeration technologies or water evaporation cooling.

Water evaporation and economizers are incredibly efficient and may seem like the most economical option, but in geographical zones where water is scarce, they may have more of an impact than initially realized. Depending on the geography, water intake can be massive—3 million to 5 million gallons of water per day—which is then treated with chemicals to reduce bacteria and manage mineral content. The water is recycled through the system 2–3 times, and 30–40% is lost to evaporation. The remaining amount is then flushed into a municipal wastewater system. Even in areas with abundant water, there is a cost associated with the treated water waste. We need to ask ourselves if water cooling technologies need to be abandoned in the future, but for now, they remain a major consideration for site selection.

Other key considerations surrounding data center site selection relate to the site's fitness to house a data center and its proximity to necessary resources. Consider average commute times for employees, access to public transportation, and trails for cycling or jogging to work for environmental impact and employee wellness. I recommend developing a scorecard with all of the factors involved in choosing a site and weighting them according to your priorities. Here are a few factors I believe should make the list:

- Chance of natural disasters (consider floodplains and liquefaction)
- Distance to connectivity
- Renewable energy availability
- Water impact
- Environment (particularly climate [temperature, humidity])
- Transportation options for workers
- Overall site fitness (developing a site requires investment in resiliency and remediation, and can increase your carbon footprint)

When it comes to our data center site choices, it is time we put the environmental impact on par or above cost considerations and begin thinking holistically about sustainability, resiliency, and cost. Putting as much importance on environmental impacts as we do on costs is a paradigm shift that needs to occur.

Energy - Indirect Carbon Emissions

Primary sources of energy today are coal-fired power plants, or what we call simple cycle, and combined cycle power plants that use sources such as gas and steam, which produce 50% more electricity than simple cycle plants. Nuclear and hydro energy are also available in many areas of the country. Nuclear energy has fallen out of favor for various reasons, even though it has incredible merits. Once constructed and deployed, nuclear reactors emit zero emissions and are the most energy-dense, resilient, and long-term sources of power currently available. Hydro generated production has also fallen out of favor for various environmental concerns due to waterways and wildlife impact. Solar energy and wind farms are now becoming commonplace and hold great promise for producing vast amounts of renewable energy and low carbon emissions, though they are not presently as energy-dense and resilient as other sources.

New technologies that I expect to develop over the next 10-200 years range from hydrogen to nuclear fusion, which may prove to be the cleanest energy produced. Scientists are developing incredible technology around fusion, which could promise limitless green electricity and uses small amounts of fuel that can be sourced with inexpensive materials.

But for now, let's get back to solar, an energy source that has seen explosive growth in recent years. Data centers have several avenues available during daylight hours to contribute to reducing carbon emissions, such as installing solar panels on buildings, parking lot structures, or in fields. In some cases, data centers have taken brave steps to create their own solar farms. The challenge that cannot be ignored is the storage of renewable energy for those hours that solar—or wind—are not immediately available. For this reason, data centers must still rely on simple or combined cycle power creation while finding ways to offset this traditional energy usage.

Providers can work with local energy suppliers to gain access to their renewable energy programs and renewable energy credits (RECs), which are essentially a method of transferring energy created with a renewable resource to the user. If your energy supplier doesn't provide RECs, it's time to evaluate your site selection decision. Joining into a REC program with your energy provider is a great way to promote local renewable sources for your region, and a data center can produce massive demand to accelerate the adoption, which will reduce costs over time.

Customer sited power purchase agreements (PPAs) are another great avenue to reduce carbon emissions. A PPA is a tool to partner with a private entity that purchases, installs, owns, operates, and maintains customer sited renewable equipment. There are also non-customer sited PPAs available, where a data center can purchase PPA credits to offset their carbon emissions. An example would be when a data center in State A has no availability of locally-sourced renewable energy and partners with State B, which is 2,000 miles away producing renewable energy. By purchasing offsets, or PPA credits from State B, State A can negate their emissions. This method is better than nothing, but not optimal. Yes, it assists with carbon emissions nationally or even regionally, but not locally. By working with local providers to accelerate renewable energy plans, you are not only improving local communities where you operate but encouraging other businesses to participate.

Exhaust - Direct Carbon Emissions

A data center's role is to provide 100% uptime, and operators spend millions in infrastructure and design to build resiliency into the system. Being prepared for outages, requires readiness and seamless remediation. To that end, we acquire and install power backup generators to operate in times of the outages.

The most common fuels used for these power generators are diesel fuel, natural gas and some experimental situations with hydrogen. Diesel and natural gas are the most prolific.

The pros of diesel generators are that they can be used virtually anywhere, they are low maintenance and have long lifespans. Diesel is also less flammable than natural gas, so the chances of an explosion or fire are lower. The cons are that diesel generators are generally more expensive, often noisier, and have higher emissions than natural gas generators. When using diesel generators, many cities now require selective catalytic reduction equipment with diesel oxidation catalysts. These devices can reduce nitrous oxide emissions by more than 70%, and carbon monoxide emissions by more than 90%. I encourage data center builders to install this equipment without being required to do so by a government agency.

Natural gas generators, on the other hand, have several pros. They burn fuel very cleanly and thus have little to no emissions. The fuel travels through underground pipes and doesn't need to be stored on site. Cons to natural gas generators are their emission of carbon dioxide, and the fact that storms and earthquakes can disrupt the supply lines.

In both cases, natural gas and diesel fuel are non-renewable types of energy. In the future, it is likely that we will see energy storage developed to act in the same role as the non-renewable generators of today, fueled by renewable energy. Many experimental technologies are being developed to address this issue.

Building Design

When it comes to the building itself, don't underestimate the costliness and potential energy loss that can occur from careless construction. Consider using devices to spot hot and cold air spots and address them with seals or fitment to avoid air leaks and loss.

We all know the environmental benefits that shopping at our

local farmer's markets can have to cut down on unnecessary food transport. Put this concept into practice at your data center by sourcing as many local materials and manufacturers as possible to reduce air and noise pollution on the local community.

Insulation is often overlooked in data centers. In Novva's Utah data center — the facility I mentioned earlier that was built from the ground-up with sustainability in mind — we have almost 3 feet of insulation between the data center and the exterior. Our walls are 14-inch thick concrete that include 4 inches of insulation. We employ basalt-based insulation on other various interior walls that protect against the loss of cooling but also reduce noise and increase fire protection. Altogether, these seemingly small considerations can create big impacts for the greening of your data center.

Cooling

How to cool the air to the servers and efficiently remove heat from the data center continues to be one of the biggest challenges in the industry. The pervasive method is oriented around using water-based cooling utilizing evaporation and economizers. Water is a low-cost, reliable resource, thus data centers gravitate to it. Water consumption, however, has a substantial impact on the environment over time and should be considered on the same level as carbon emission energy sources.

To put data centers' water usage in perspective, a 1MW data center can consume up to 6.6 million gallons of water per year, while the typical American household consumes an estimated 3,600 gallons per year. That means a 1MW data center uses the equivalent water of 1,833 households per year and a 100 MW data center would use the equivalent of 183,300 homes.

Water is not only problematic in consumption but in the wastewater it produces and oftentimes, municipal sewage systems are not equipped to handle such volume or the proper treatment of it.

Cooling efficiency can be a combination of multiple factors:

- Site location
- Required operating temperatures for server effectiveness
- Building design
- Compute density
- Humidity levels
- Cooling technology employed

Two key metrics used by many data centers are power usage effectiveness (PUE), which measures the ratio between power drawn by the computer infrastructure and cooling energy, and water usage effectiveness (WUE), a similar metric used to calculate the ratio of power drawn for compute infrastructure or the amount of water consumed in liters to kWh. Data centers need to measure both of these metrics and improve the effectiveness of cooling to compute. Perhaps your facility is colder than it needs to be and raising operating temperatures can have an immediate, positive impact on efficiency. Work with clients to find operating temperatures that are adaptable for both parties and create financial incentives cooperatively. The American Society of Heating, Refrigerating and Air-Conditioning Engineers (ASHRAE) recommends operating temperatures of 64 degrees to 81 degrees in normal environments, and 64 degrees to 69.8 degrees in environments with low levels of copper and silver corrosion.

I'm hopeful that over time, semiconductor and server manufacturers improve the efficiency of power consumption to compute ratio, and thus reduce the amount of cooling necessary to maintain the effectiveness of the equipment. The average cabinet power usage has grown from 2kW per cabinet in 2007 to 12.5kW in 2022, and it is not unusual to now see cabinets consuming 30kW to 50kW. As compute loads per square feet have risen, so have the cooling requirements, and the subsequent size and amount of equipment needed to cool such dense compute.

Waterless Cooling

There are cooling choices other than water-oriented solutions that can be employed cost effectively. By creating air-cooled chillers with larger exposed coils, you can expand the number of hours and temperatures that you can take in ambient air. In Novva's Utah data center, we are able to operate our free cool or partial cool hours up to 95% of the year, and only operate on mechanical chilling 5% of the year. The mechanical portion is a combination of recycling heated air within the data center through heat exchange coils, converting it back to cold air, or using refrigerant to cool the closed loop system, which contains water without chemicals.

The chilling system is not enough on its own. The entire ecosystem must be considered, including containment. Avoid mixing hot and cold air and use a closed-circuit hot air return for further efficiencies.

It's essential to reduce water consumption and pursue aggressive strategies to employ new technologies. HVAC technologies for data centers are just slightly evolved from building and manufacturing HVAC approaches; therefore, the data center industry needs to innovate on this front. Choosing a site that is compatible with lower temperatures will go a long way to resolving this issue so that ambient free cooled air can be utilized more proportionally.

Steps Every Data Center Can Take on Their Greener Data Journey

Aside from these big, impactful decisions, little day-to-day changes can make a big difference on the path to greener data centers. Here are four small strategies you can employ almost immediately:

1. Embrace remote work for employees who can perform their work from home. I have always subscribed to the idea that employees don't work for me, they work with

me. Improve their quality of life through reduced stress, lower carbon emissions from vehicles, and reduced traffic.

2. Avoid single-use plastics at all costs. Provide filtered water stations in convenient locations throughout the office, along with recyclable containers.

3. Recycle bins should be standard office equipment. The more conveniently they are located, the more often they will get used.

4. Provide electric charging stations that are convenient for clients and employees. If corporate vehicles are a necessity, set an example by purchasing electric vehicles. There are a plethora of choices in the market today, from cars, trucks, utility vehicles, scooters, and bikes.

In summary, there are many changes that data centers can make, which can influence others in the industry and the communities where they reside. Reduced pollution and conservation impact the health of our planet and everyone living on it, including future generations.

I believe that data center designers, builders, and operators can be catalysts for change and still prosper economically. Let's take a humanistic and holistic view of our impacts and how we can lessen them. It should become a part of our culture and lexicon without becoming a lecture.

Finally, if you are a client of a data center, demand more of your enterprise and your operator. Let them know that sustainability is an important factor for you and your company. You would be surprised at how effective your voice can be. Look at Woodsy Owl from 1977! His little voice still reverberates inside my mind when I choose to recycle. Let us be the collective voice for the next generations to come.

———————————————————

1. ITU. "Statistics." ITU. https://www.itu.int/en/ITU-D/Statistics/Pages/stat/default.aspx.

2. Kamiya, George. 2021. "Data Centres and Data Transmission Networks." IEA. November 2021. https://www.iea.org/reports/data-centres-and-data-transmission-networks.

3. TeleGeography. 2021. "Global Internet Geography Executive Summary." TeleGeography Global Internet Geography, PriMetrica, Inc. https://www2.telegeography.com/hubfs/assets/product-tear-sheets/product-page-content-samples/global-internet-geography/telegeography-global-internet-geography-executive-summary.pdf.

About the Author

WES SWENSON

Wes is a founder, investor, and the CEO of Novva, as well as the former CEO and founder of Utah-based C7 Data Centers (acquired by DataBank in 2017). With 35 years of experience working in the tech industry—including 15 years in the data center industry—Wes has a deep knowledge of technology including: semi-conductors, desktop software, network software and hardware, web security, consumer products, and data centers.

NINETEEN

Jennifer von Bismarck

DATA AND ITS ROLE IN THE SUSTAINABLE INVESTING ECOSYSTEM

Acknowledgement

This chapter is written with gratitude for the support and input from iM Data Centers, SmartAC.com, Innovateus Solar, Hive, and Sarene Marshall, Chief Sustainability Officer of Galway Sustainable Capital.

Data and its Role in the Sustainable Investing Ecosystem

At Galway, we are a specialty finance company focused on sustainable investments. Some people might tell you that we provide project financing for green infrastructure, but we have a larger goal: our team is passionate about investing to drive a transition toward greater environmental and social impact across economic ecosystems. At first glance, Galway's approach may confuse some. Infrastructure? Project finance? Impact? The capital markets are typically organized by asset classes. Fund managers are expected to invest in distinct industry silos. Our firm has taken a different approach to this thinking.

In his 1990 book *The Fifth Discipline*, MIT professor Peter Senge explained that systems thinking is the key to becoming a learning organization. He wrote that "…from an early age we are taught to break apart problems, to fragment the world. This apparently makes complex tasks and subjects more manageable, but we pay a hidden, enormous price. We can no longer see the consequences of our actions: we lose our intrinsic sense of connection to a larger whole." While Senge was speaking about successful companies, his observations have much broader application.

When we observe the trajectory of economic growth around the world and we see the resulting impact on the planet today, it is clear that driving sustainability requires systems thinking, not just in the way we build businesses, but also in the way we assemble these businesses into an economy; and in the way the economy interacts with the natural world.

Galway's approach to investing involves (eco)systems thinking. That means we look at key aspects of human interaction with nature and think about how to make that relationship more sustainable. We consider the connections among real assets and communities. We know that the projects we finance are going to have an impact on land, water, air quality, and energy use. Depending on where and how assets are located, built, and owned, there will be impacts on equity, health, and access to opportunity. We look for investments that will make a positive transition toward greater sustainability within the surrounding human and natural ecosystems. Data is a key element of nearly every economic ecosystem today.

Data: The Information Economy's Hidden Price

The industrial economy, with its focus on utilizing natural resources and burning fossil fuels, created many of the environmental and social ills we are now trying to undo. The information economy holds promises of reducing environmental impacts in the world and generating social benefits. Virtual meetings can replace the high carbon footprint of airline travel and overcome economic and geographic barriers of bringing people together.

Digital records enable us to keep and share information without cutting down trees or shipping heavy books. Technology can help us monitor our energy use and use less of it, access education, improve our health, and open a world of new jobs.

In our quest for efficiency, humans are increasingly turning to technology (in smart cars, smart devices, and smart cities) that can give us information to make better decisions. But these digital solutions are not impact-free. There is a devil in the details, and it's called data. By 2025, 42 billion devices are estimated to be connected to the internet. The data collected by all these devices – estimated at a staggering 79.4 zettabytes – must be stored somewhere.[1] That storage – unlike a book on a library shelf – requires power. Accessing and analyzing the data requires yet more power – not brain-power, but increasingly computing power.

In trying to solve the sustainability challenge, we must take care not to inadvertently create new problems. Unlike black plumes emerging from smokestacks or mountains of trash in land-fills, we do not generally *see* the impacts of the data we create and store, perhaps outside of our cluttered email inboxes. It's easy to forget about the invisible data needs of devices and systems that should help us use resources wisely, make good decisions, and improve people's lives. As environmentally-minded participants in the information economy, we must take our data footprint into account. Depending on how green our data is, the carbon from data can add up.

In Galway's own portfolio, we have businesses focused on energy-efficient buildings, electric vehicles, and renewable power – all leading solutions in sustainable infrastructure. But we know these systems generate data that must be stored, processed, and utilized – lots of it. So, another one of our investment areas is in energy efficient data centers, powered with renewable energy. Just as systems thinking supports a learning organization, green data ensures that smart devices can be green devices.

Data Efficiency is Energy Efficiency

The ability to measure, monitor, and control our energy-consuming devices underpins more efficient resource use. And buildings are major consumers of energy – 40% of the U.S.' total energy use in 2020, with heating and cooling (HVAC) and lighting systems responsible for much of this footprint. When systems are not operating optimally, they run more than they need to, consuming significantly more electricity. Beyond energy, HVAC units have another big environmental impact, and that is through the refrigerants they contain, which are potent greenhouse gases. As systems age, these gases can leak into the atmosphere, speeding up climate change.

Smart controls for building systems are an essential part of the transition to greater sustainability. As part of our strategy, Galway invested in SmartAC.com, a Texas-based company that manufactures and installs devices to monitor the performance of residential HVAC units.

These sensors, part of the now ubiquitous Internet of Things (IoT), provide valuable information about the health and operating status of HVAC units, so that they can be controlled and maintained more efficiently. Sensor data allows customers to replace filters on a timely basis and allows repair technicians to keep systems working in good order, eliminating unnecessary energy use or damage due to water or coolant leaks or other system failures.

Because of advancements in software and processing capacity, devices like SmartAC.com's can capture mountains of data. But when considering the power implications of storing, accessing, and processing data, we should ask: how much is enough? By some estimates, only 1% of IoT data collected is actually used.[2] That is not only an astonishing amount of potentially wasted data, but also wasted energy needed to store it on servers running 24-7 in data centers – buildings that need to be lighted and cooled.

As SmartAC.com worked to improve its product, it also optimized the interval at which data packets are processed and uploaded to the cloud. Its goal was to gather the minimum amount of data needed to achieve its business objectives. While it was possible to capture and send data every 2 seconds, the company realized that not only was a significant amount of that data not needed, but also that the process of capturing and storing it would also shorten battery life. At 10 second intervals, the business objectives could easily be met, but each HVAC unit was generating 5.8 GB of data per year that needed to be stored. The cost of storage and the decreased battery life would lead to wasted materials, energy, and money. As a result, the company started applying the concept of efficiency to their data capture. Over the past year, given a significantly increased number of units deployed in the field providing a larger data set and ever-improving accuracy of detection and diagnosis of residential HVAC issues, SmartAC.com has been able to increase the interval at which it collects information to 20 seconds, which almost halves the data captured. The company plans to optimize its system and cut the amount of data generated per unit even further, without sacrificing decision outcomes, by using capabilities built into their firmware to dynamically adjust the data collection frequency by sensor, enabling polling of some sensors as infrequently as every few minutes while others are scaled up and down; never sacrificing business objectives while improving battery life and reducing environmental impact. As we transition to a more sustainable economy, companies like SmartAC.com are showing that for smart controls to be successful, they need to be cost efficient and energy efficient, which means they also need to be data efficient.

Data-Driven Vehicles

Transportation is essential in modern society, but it comes with numerous negative impacts. In the United States, the sector is the leading contributor to climate change, responsible for 29% of greenhouse gas emissions, more than half of those from passenger and light-duty vehicles. Gas-powered vehicles also spew tailpipe pollution that causes health problems. To combat these challenges, governments are setting zero-emission vehicle goals. A leading way to achieve those goals is to couple electric vehicles (EVs) with renewable electricity.

From California to the White House to the UN Climate Conference (COP-26), 2021 witnessed dozens of governments, manufacturers and fleet owners, and other groups connected to the automotive industry, pledging to transition to zero-emissions vehicles by the 2030s. Federal U.S. legislation, including the 2021 Infrastructure Bill, contains billions approved or proposed for a national charging network, domestic EV manufacturing, consumer tax credits, and more.

We cannot meet these goals simply by making more EVs. Today, compared to gas options, EVs are more costly up front. There is also a shortage of convenient charging facilities, especially for apartment-dwellers and people in disadvantaged communities.

The solution isn't just in volume, but it is also in making EV's affordable and accessible. To accelerate adoption of EVs and diversify the drivers using them, Galway invested in Hive, a company that provides people who drive for Uber and Door Dash the ability to rent EVs on flexible terms that make these cars more affordable. Not only is Hive expanding access, but they are committed to a leading low-carbon strategy. As Energy Secretary Jennifer Granholm said "EVs are only as clean as the electrons going into them," and Hive is also building an EV charging network for their drivers that is powered with 100% renewable energy, converting the highest utilization drivers to truly zero-emission electric vehicles.

As we work to optimize access and emissions from the transportation sector, we are mindful of the data footprint of the sector. In the next wave of smart transportation, manufacturers are expanding automated driving features. These computer-assisted vehicles have sensors that capture vast amounts of real-time data, from both inside and outside the vehicle. This data feeds systems to improve the driving experience, enhance safety, and even help the transportation industry evolve towards fully autonomous driving. Companies like Hive can use this data from vehicles and pair it with information from gig economy apps to optimize vehicle maintenance and insurance while improving services for drivers. This involves a lot of onboard data generation, and a significant amount of data for offloading and computing. A vehicle operating with basic self-driving features today generates approximately 25 GB of data per hour.[3] Once we have fully autonomous vehicles (AVs), it is likely that they will generate and transmit, on average, one terabyte (TB) of data per hour.[4] The auto industry is essentially undergoing a transition from being gas-powered to being data-powered. With it, there will be a tsunami of new data that swells into existence, and that data will require energy to store and analyze.

Estimates vary on just how much energy this implies. As we evaluated the data footprint within our portfolio, we estimated how much power it would take to store all the bytes created. Depending on the circumstances, it takes approximately 2.5 kw of power to store 5 petabytes of data, or roughly 0.5 watts of power for each terabyte. At the rate of 0.5 watts per hour per car, simply storing the data from autonomous driving could imply gigawatts of computing power over the course of a year. The potential for all this new data underscores why our data centers need to be energy-efficient and carbon-neutral.

Solar Energy and its Data Shadow

Accelerating deployment of renewable power is a key solution to the climate crisis. With this goal in mind, Galway has made significant investments in solar energy. We have over 3 GW of potential clean power opportunities available through our portfolio companies, including Inovateus Solar – a South Bend, Indiana company that was founded in 2008. Inovateus develops, builds, and owns solar projects that serve utilities, municipalities, electric cooperatives, schools, universities, and commercial customers throughout the Midwest, Mid-Atlantic, and Northeast.

As Inovateus and others bring their projects online, we get

the thrill of watching them connect to the grid. When their remote monitoring systems are turned on, we can log in to a portal and see – in real- time – how many megawatts are being generated. As these green electrons offset dirty ones from coal- and gas-fired electricity, we feel great. This is how clean-energy investors might typically count their carbon impact. But our ability to watch and measure these results means that something else is happening.

A solar plant consists of individual sun-grabbing panels, each equipped with an inverter. The facility's communication system must allow multiple devices to be connected to the same network. The network then connects via cellular to cloud-based data storage and processing centers that enable remote monitoring, making it fast and easy to observe energy production from anywhere. But what about the data and energy implications of all this information? As an ecosystem investor, we know that even the build-out of clean electricity must also consider the footprint of the data it creates.

Power plants sell electricity to the grid around the clock. That means systems must be monitored 24 hours per day, 365 days per year, or 8,760 hours per year. With power typically priced and traded in increments of 15 minutes, an interconnected facility generates 35,040 (4 x 8,760) blocks of energy annually. To calculate the output from a solar farm, each panel reports its status. A one-megawatt facility will have 2,500 400-watt panels, each sending out and storing information about its generation. At a typical solar data generation rate, we estimate that each megawatt of solar installed will produce 25 megabytes to 5 gigabytes of data per year to be stored. That means a gigawatt of installed solar could generate less data in a year than a self-driving car generates *every hour.* Thankfully, solar's data footprint is just a shadow compared to that of AVs.

For many reasons, solar energy is a critical component of a more sustainable economy. While it is a very data efficient form of power, we must still work to eliminate emissions from all sources. As we bring renewable energy online, we can use it to power data centers, setting us on a pathway for green data to support all types of clean and smart tech.

The need to incorporate green data into our portfolio led us to invest in iM Data Centers, based in Sunrise, Florida.

The Green Data Backbone

We met the CEO of iM Data Centers in Pittsburgh in late 2020 where he was planning his first US-based modular data center campus. We were enthusiastic about his proposal for a highly energy efficient facility that could be factory-built, installed on-site, and powered with 100% renewable energy. In addition to deploying its own portfolio of right-sized colocation facilities at key locations in the US, iM also repurposes older inefficient data centers into modern, state-of-the-art data centers. iM's offering fits a critical need in our portfolio. We knew that we had to have an answer to green data if we were going to build a portfolio of smart climate solutions that ran on IoT.

As we considered adding data centers to our portfolio, we were mindful that just as smart cities use data, smart data centers use cities, or more specifically, land and resources. We wanted to make sure our investment in sustainable data was also thoughtful about land use, materials, and impact on the community. iM's modular units can be sited in unused commercial spaces or even parking lots where their impact on the existing land is minimal. They are scalable so that the initial install can be right-sized to the current need, while allowing for seamless expansion as necessary. The factory-built process allows iM to use better quality materials and generate less waste, less noise and less particulate and other air pollution during construction. In addition, factory jobs at iM provide safer, more comfortable work environments than site builds, which opens up the fabrication opportunity to a more diverse workforce. (For more information, see iM's chapter in this book.)

Investing — Smart Ecosystems for a Sustainable Economy

We are working to apply the lessons learned across our portfolio, including in renewable energy, mobility and green buildings. Being an ESG investor means we apply two filters to our investment opportunities. First, we must evaluate the links between activities within the economic system. Second, we must evaluate the links between the economic system, the environment, and people. Both points help us evaluate risk. When we make investments in companies that have shared or aligned interests, they are better positioned to help one another succeed. As an example, now that we have identified a great team who develops and constructs solar power, that team can help our other portfolio companies access 100% renewable power, lower their energy costs, and improve their carbon footprint. These are valuable links within the economic system of projects. When we also consider the impact these companies have on the planet, we think about whether these projects bring benefits to the environment and to the people in the communities where these projects will operate. These factors help us understand the potential longevity of these businesses, and the potential for future costs that they might incur. In a competitive job market, our companies perform better when they provide desirable places to work. We believe this ecosystem mindset helps us maximize long-term value and enhance risk-adjusted returns.

Over the past 200 years, the world has transformed itself. The human population has grown from around 1 billion people to over 7 billion and greenhouse gases have nearly doubled in their atmospheric concentrations. Humans innovated their way into the industrial revolution and all the way through the space race to expand what is possible on earth and even outside our atmosphere. Knowledge workers invented and exploded the information economy to create learning organizations and artificially intelligent machines. The next critical step in this evolution is to apply our ingenuity to systems thinking about our impact on the world around us, including of the data we create and depend on. Peter Senge reminded us over 30 years ago that systems thinking forces us to see the consequences of our actions. Right now, systems thinking means linking the health of the economy to the health of the environment. Investing in systemic change requires using a systems mindset as part of the investment process. This fifth discipline is now more critical than ever, as we work to transform the economy and the planet into something that is sustainable.

---

1. Pratt, Mary K. 2020. "Understand IoT Data Storage Options for Data Deluge." IoT Agenda. TechTarget. March 18, 2020. https://internetofthingsagenda.techtarget.com/tip/Understand-IoT-data-storage-options-for-data-deluge.
2. Goldberg, Stephen. 2018. "Preventing IoT Data Waste with the Intelligent Edge." TechTarget. April 2, 2018. https://internetofthingsagenda.techtarget.com/blog/IoT-Agenda/Preventing-IoT-data-waste-with-the-intelligent-edge.
3. Wright, Simon. 2021. "Autonomous Cars Generate More than 300 TB of Data per Year." Tuxera. July 2, 2021. https://www.tuxera.com/blog/autonomous-cars-300-tb-of-data-per-year/.
4. Götz, Florian. 2021. "The Data Deluge: What do we do with the data generated by AVs?" Siemens. January 22, 2021. https://blogs.sw.siemens.com/polarion/the-data-deluge-what-do-we-do-with-the-data-generated-by-avs/.

About the Author

JENNIFER VON BISMARCK

Jennifer von Bismarck is a founding partner and CEO of Galway Sustainable Capital ("GSC"). Galway is a specialty finance company investing in companies that bring about positive environmental and social impact. Founded in 2020, GSC is directing hundreds of millions of dollars into companies engaged in transitioning food, land, water, energy, buildings, transportation, and goods and services toward more sustainable solutions.

Prior to forming GSC, Ms. Von Bismarck served as an investment partner in Galway II, III, and IV, as well as affiliated entities, TowPath Partners and ARENA Investments (collectively the "Galway Companies"). These prior investment enterprises served to originate, underwrite, and acquire niche non-correlated assets in structured credit as well as sustainability. She served on investment committees of these entities, helped lead the acquisition of $2 billion in financial assets, and oversaw the issuance of over $1 billion in debt and private placements.

Before her work with the Galway Companies, she served as the second team member hired to manage the personal net worth of Microsoft chairman Bill Gates. Ms. von Bismarck serves on the board of Partnership for Responsible Growth, a non-profit organization working to establish a regulated price on carbon. She holds a BA from Mount Holyoke and an MBA from Cornell University.

TWENTY

Vicki L. Worden

GREENER DATA: A CRITICAL ELEMENT SUPPORTING ESG AND DECARBONIZATION

Understanding the impacts, demands, and opportunity for greener data in the 21st century requires an understanding of big picture trends impacting all levels of organizational planning from the boardroom to the remotest facility. Data now connects every informed decision from how to write and structure annual reports to when to retrofit HVAC and lighting systems. Data collection and management systems are critical to achieving our global environmental objectives.

The Green Building Initiative (GBI) is an international, mission-based organization focused on reducing climate impacts by improving the built environment. Drawing on the experience of certifying a half a billion square feet of commercial buildings for some of the largest portfolio owners in the world, this chapter is GBI's view on the integral role of greener data in decision-making toward greener buildings and portfolios.

ESG and Decarbonization Tipping Points Collide in the 21st Century

Environmental, social, and governance (ESG) reporting can be more easily thought of as three related concepts: sustainability, social responsibility, and transparency in governance. In 2020, Europe adopted new regulations governing ESG reporting and how it should be defined for the purpose of investment decision-making. This development was deemed a tipping point by Colliers, a global leader in real estate investment and services, signaling that "ESG is no longer an option, it's a 'must have.'"[1] The EU regulations were driven by recognition that it will take top down commitments of organizations and governments to achieve 2030 global climate and energy targets, driven largely by the urgent need to reduce carbon emissions. Nothing drives change more than a call to action from investors combined with regulatory action of governments, which is exactly what has led to the collision of ESG and decarbonization tipping points.

Within every organization, there is a renewed impetus to ensure that goals, objectives, and public commitments are accompanied by transparent reporting of key performance indicators (KPIs), ongoing action plans, and accountability for results. Data —and that is data from throughout organizations and supply chains, including of course utility data as just one small component of the overall need—is now critical to operational and investment objectives from this point forward.

Toward this end, global businesses are making public commitments to achieving net-zero carbon emissions within the next nine to twenty-nine years and partnering throughout their businesses and spheres of influence to create lasting change. High profile examples of these commitments include:

- **Amazon** – Amazon co-founded The Climate Pledge, which has led to 200 additional signatories agreeing to pursue carbon-reduction activities to achieve net-zero carbon emissions by 2040.

- **Google** – Google committed to decarbonizing its energy consumption to be carbon-free energy, everywhere, 24/7, by 2030. Google's Environmental Insights Explorer (EIE) was launched in 2018 as a free online tool available to 3,000 cities to provide data sources and modeling capabilities to help policymakers measure and reduce emissions.
- **Microsoft** – Microsoft plans to be carbon negative by 2030 and by 2050, to remove from the environment "all of the carbon the company has emitted either directly or by electrical consumption since it was founded in 1975."[2] Microsoft also will use its technology to reduce its own footprint and it plans to invest in carbon reduction, capture, and removal technologies.
- **Marriott International** – Marriott committed to the Science-Based Targets initiative to reach net-zero value chain greenhouse gas (GHG) emissions by no later than 2050. This multinational corporations' "SERVE 360: Doing Good in Every Direction" program further commits 100% of its Marriott International hotels to having green building or sustainability certification by 2025 and requires top contracted suppliers to provide information on product sustainability.[3]
- **BlackRock** – BlackRock supports the goal of reducing GHG emissions by 2050 and has helped to establish Decarbonization Partners, a $600 million partnership to invest in companies providing solutions that reduce carbon emissions. In 2021, BlackRock CEO Larry Fink observed that in 2020, global investment in sustainable assets totaled $288 billion, a 96% increase over 2019, and predicted "a long but rapidly accelerating transition" towards sustainable investing.[4]
- **Blackstone** – Blackstone announced a goal in 2021

to reduce carbon emissions by 15% across all new investments where it controls energy usage and is creating a pipeline that will lead to 300 megawatts of on-site solar power across its real-estate portfolio by 2025.[5] Within its many business units, its logistics unit —Link Logistics Real Estate, one of the biggest operators of industrial property in the U.S.—says it will be carbon neutral by 2025.[6] (See Blackstone's 2021 "An Integrated Approach to ESG" as an example of high-level ESG reporting.)[7]

Additionally, twenty-two U.S. states currently have net-zero commitments,[8] and more than 130 countries have now set or are considering a target of reducing emissions to net zero by 2050.[9] Net-zero commitments cover one-fifth of the world's largest corporations and 68% of global GDP, compared to just 16% in 2019.[10] Investor communities are doing their part with Goldman Sachs, Vanguard, JP Morgan Chase, and Fidelity making commitments and the Glasgow Financial Alliance for Net Zero, a coalition of financial institutions that holds $130 trillion worth of assets, committing to supporting countries and companies in decarbonization.

"An Integrated Approach to ESG" © Blackstone 2021

Where commitments abound, there are also concerns about measurement of results and avoiding "greenwashing." ESG reporting expectations level the playing field. While there are no mandatory ESG disclosures at the federal level in the United States, there are plenty of signals that they are imminent, including statements to this effect by Securities and Exchange Commissioner (SEC) Gary Gensler. The SEC is expected to require companies to disclose both qualitative and quantitative sustainability data, such as physical and transition risks of climate change and significant impacts on the economy, environment, and people when considering what is a "materiality" concern for investors.

From tech giants to real estate giants, data will be central to our collective success in achieving decarbonization ambitions. The combined focus on ESG reporting at an investor level with the ever-increasing likelihood of government definitions and require-ments means that traditional corporate social responsibility and sustainability reports are morphing into overall ESG reports. ESG reporting requires defensible data. It requires a commitment throughout organizational systems—from financing and acquisition to leasing and facility management, as an example. It requires a culture that instills in associates and key influencers a passion to uphold and reinforce those systems and requirements. This tipping point of ESG integration and commitment to decarbonization will be fed by a consistent flow of data throughout organizations and into the hands of stakeholders.

How ESG Supports Net Zero Ambitions

These are ambitious targets, and reaching them requires a framework that can measure emissions, reimagine and restructure operations to reduce them, and consistently monitor results and adapt accordingly. To supplement emissions objectives, investors are increasingly holding companies accountable to a range of social and equity targets as well. Their charge is not only to reduce emissions, but to do so while enhancing lives and communities.

At the corporate level, there is a need for a framework that can measure all of these priorities, provide a path forward, and gather and distribute meaningful data across all targets. Corporate initiatives intended to reduce environmental harm have existed for a long time. Corporate Sustainability (CS), which first entered the lexicon in the 1970s, introduced the idea that companies should pay attention to the "triple bottom line" of people, planet, and profit. In practice, CS tended to focus on environmental performance and frequently lacked a commitment to KPIs. Corporate Social Responsibility (CSR) came later, adding an emphasis on accountability to the public and stakeholders. CSR is frequently thought of as oriented towards reputation management, and, like its predecessor, often lacked meaningful KPIs.

Neither of these frameworks is robust enough—or data-oriented enough—to provide a pathway toward achieving net zero. ESG differs. ESG focuses on the entire range of non-financial issues that influence a company's performance and impact. Among its innovations are the introduction of governance as the key to performance and a focus on measuring and reporting KPIs. Unlike its predecessors, ESG frameworks can provide a path towards decarbonization that increases profitability, supports social and equity goals, and provides data and reporting to support its claims.

"What is ESG?" © Green Building Initiative 2021

Critically, ESG also possesses both a risk management and a value creation orientation. In addition to environmental measurements, it covers social issues including diversity, equity, and inclusion, employee and occupant satisfaction, and stakeholder engagement, as well as governance issues including ethics and risk disclosures. One of the inherent strengths of an ESG framework is that in acknowledging the intersection of a company's environmental and social impacts with its governance structure, ESG systems offer benefits that extend far beyond supporting the pursuit of one goal, providing companies with a framework that increases their competitive advantage across the board, improves resilience, and reduces risk.

ESG as a Competitive Advantage

Companies that pursue decarbonization goals lower their energy costs which increases profitability. They may also avoid regulation or achieve deregulation, and, by remaining in front of policy shifts toward efficiency, they are positioned to outpace competitors who are forced to react to policy changes after they happen. Companies with strong ESG performance also accrue long-term advantages like climate resilience and positioning for the changing energy future, and a strong governing structure reduces their organizational risk exposure over time.

Finally, these companies also gain reputation and public relations advantages, both internally and externally. Research shows that ESG commitments increasingly attract and retain a talented workforce and help to motivate employees. Investors also see strong ESG performance as a measure of overall company health and projected long-term stability. Therefore, investors are increasingly applying these non-financial factors as part of their analysis process to identify material risks and growth opportunities with the objective of reducing exposure to investments that pose greater ESG risks and influencing companies to become more sustainable. Numerous institutions, such as the Sustainability Accounting Standards Board (SASB), the Global Reporting Initiative (GRI), and the Task Force on Climate-related Financial Disclosures (TCFD) have frameworks and definitions around materiality to facilitate incorporation of these factors into the investment process.[11]

Green Building Certification and ESG Reporting

In the real estate sector, Global Real Estate Sustainability Benchmark (GRESB) is a mission-driven and investor-led organization that is a global leader in ESG benchmarking for real estate assets. The GRESB framework ranks portfolios on key measures of materiality within the real estate sector—both Management and Development, or Management and Performance—and participation in the organization results in a rank versus peers. Within GRESB, commitments to energy and carbon emissions reductions must be described both qualitatively and quantitatively. This means that utility data must be collected and energy transition projects must be documented along with corporate commitments, examples of stakeholder engagement, and links to transparent reporting.

Implementation of ESG across a building portfolio is also measured in part by third-party validated achievements, such as achieving building certification under the U.S. EPA's ENERGY STAR®, which can provide partial points through GRESB for energy-efficiency achievements. Also, using the Green Building Initiative's Green Globes® certification on a building or portfolio can achieve a greater number of points under GRESB[12] as a holistic certification that recognizes five additional considerations beyond energy including site, materials, water, indoor environment, and ESG management or project management. Achieving certifications like Green Globes and providing validated energy and carbon emissions reduction data across a large portion of a portfolio can increase the rank or rating of that portfolio versus its competitors.

Data drives every aspect of measuring commitments, and ESG reports cover everything from energy efficiency strategies to corporate DEI achievements and from alignment with ESG frameworks to all other aspects of governance and oversight.

ESG, Net Zero, and the Data & Telecommunications Industry

The data and telecommunications industries enter this critical moment with a very particular set of circumstances. Approximately 2.5% of global energy is used serving data centers and data transmission networks, and this number is projected to rise quickly. In fact, it is projected that the percentage of global energy usage consumed by data centers alone will rise to 8-10% by 2030.[13] In other words, data and telecommunications not only consume a larger amount of energy already, but that amount is projected to increase exponentially year over year.

This makes decarbonization a particularly pressing priority for data and telecommunications industries. Because they are such significant consumers of energy, their participation is necessary for governments to reach net zero goals. They are also likely targets for regulatory and investment pressure, and they face high risk exposure to a changing energy future. Data and telecommunications industries are increasingly recognized as providing critical infrastructure, with system disruptions or failures having massive consequences. There is a need for data and telecom industries to scale rapidly while reducing emissions and avoiding any disruptions in service. To meet all of these goals at once, they require a framework like ESG that addresses all non-financial factors influencing a company's performance and impact while maintaining a focus on long-term profitability and risk reduction.

ESG Implementation & Data Centers

There are four major steps in implementing an ESG strategy in an organization. The first typically involves partnering with a third-party consultant or developing the talent in house to conduct a current state assessment.

1. Conduct a baseline assessment (current state)
2. Establish goals (future state)
3. Develop a roadmap & determine KPIs
4. Report progress

A current state assessment will identify gaps and opportunities across environmental, social, and governance functions. Depending on your ESG alignment goals, your consultant may conduct a materiality assessment as part of this current state. Such assessments identify the critical elements of organizational success and risk and provide a framework for the next step of setting goals.

Successful ESG programs are rooted in a company's values, and involvement of key stakeholders in initial assessments can help to reframe and reinforce those values. Aligning values and goals provides the critical elements to moving forward with an ESG strategy that is authentically connected to your principles.

Once current state and future state are established, the process of selecting meaningful KPIs becomes much easier. Best practices involve finding KPIs that align with your goals, or those things that make a material difference in your organization's success, and making a commitment to track these KPIs year over year. Consult the list below for an overview of basic data points that can feed into KPIs.

Environmental	Social	Governance
• Total carbon emissions • Total carbon capture • Total energy consumption • Total water consumption • Total waste generated • Total raw materials used • Proportion of raw materials where embodied carbon has been analyzed, are gained from recycled or biobased sources, or that have third-party certifications • Percentage of properties that have achieved ENERGY STAR® or Green Globes® certification	• Employee satisfaction, development, and retention statistics • Total number of hours spent on development and training per year • Resident/occupant satisfaction survey results • Health and safety statistics • DEI demographics of employees and vendors • Number of community engagement projects • Number of beneficiaries of community engagement	• ESG Council and accountability • Ethics and conflict of interest statements • Industry partnerships • Demographic breakdown of board and executive team • Executive compensation and other compensation disclosures • Privacy and cybersecurity • Compliance • Litigation • Risk assessment and disclosures of climate risk • Annual reporting on KPIs

Each goal and KPI can align with strategies and tactics that are assigned to teams in your organization. These teams are then accountable for feeding data back into the ESG monitoring system you put in place. Each data point also may have sub data points that require examination. For example, carbon emission measurement should involve both direct and indirect emissions as well as emission intensity. For data centers and other specific industries, the terms, units, and KPIs may be further specialized, such as power usage effectiveness (PUE), total energy cost, the occurrence and duration of hot spots, and even wastewater generated.

Data Centers, ESG & The Built Environment

Our own Green Building Initiative (GBI)'s comprehensive and cost-effective approach to certification has supported leading edge portfolio owners as they use our rating systems as roadmaps that result in Green Globes certification. These efforts identify efficiencies, provide decision-making mechanisms for each phase of a building's life cycle, and validate resulting sustainability implementation efforts. GBI also now offers advisory services that support overall ESG efforts, including providing corporate green specifications review to increase likelihood of compliance with green building objectives. Through membership, education, and credentialing as well as an inclusive global network of green building and ESG experts, GBI supports portfolio owners wherever they are in their ESG, decarbonization, and green building journeys.

A few examples of data center validation efforts include:

- Equinix, Ashburn, Virginia, USA – achieved Three Green Globes certification on two separate facilities
- CyrusOne, Aurora, Illinois, USA – achieved Three Green Globes certification on two separate facilities[14]
- Digital Realty Trust, Tempe and Chandler, Arizona, USA – achieved Two Green Globes certification on two separate facilities

These facilities set and demonstrate targets for energy and water efficiency; implement policies that include consideration of embodied carbon; use low-VOC products in purchasing;, audit and address waste practices; and follow facility maintenance practices that support ongoing efficiency outcomes. In certified buildings, there is robust monitoring of mechanical and electrical systems, comprehensive energy management and sustainability policies, green cleaning practices, and refrigerant management plans.

Conclusion

Strong ESG performance and integration of decarbonization within organizations are correlated with strong financial performance and reduced risk exposure across industries. Data drives ESG integration and is key to transparent reporting on decarbonization efforts. Within data centers, there's a need for the combination of high-level ESG expectations with empowerment of those that are on-the-ground implementing facility efficiency strategies, which should include validation of sustainability achievements through green building certification and reporting through ESG frameworks like GRESB. This combination of implementing ESG, decarbonization, data monitoring, and third-party validation can help ensure that net zero carbon ambitions become a reality.

---

1. Harrington, Damian and Neil Crook. 2021. "ESG at a tipping point." Colliers International. October 2021. https://www.colliers.com/en-dk/research/202110-esg-at-a-tipping-point.
2. Smith, Brad. 2020. "Microsoft Will Be Carbon Negative by 2030." The Official Microsoft Blog. January 16, 2020. https://blogs.microsoft.com/blog/2020/01/16/microsoft-will-be-carbon-negative-by-2030/.
3. Marriott International. https://serve360.marriott.com/.
4. Fink, Larry. 2021. "Larry Fink's 2021 letter to CEOs." BlackRock. https://www.blackrock.com/us/individual/2021-larry-fink-ceo-letter.
5. Blackstone. 2020. "Our Next Step in ESG: A New Emissions Reduction Program," September 29, 2020. Blackstone Inc. https://www.blackstone.com/insights/article/our-next-step-in-esg-a-new-emissions-reduction-program/.
6. Wong, Natalie. 2021. "Blackstone's Logistics Unit Aims for Carbon Neutrality by 2025." Bloomberg Green. February 25, 2021. https://www.bloomberg.com/news/articles/2021-02-25/blackstone-s-logistics-unit-aims-for-carbon-neutrality-by-2025.
7. Blackstone. 2021. "An Integrated Approach to ESG." Blackstone. November 2021. https://www.blackstone.com/wp-content/uploads/sites/2/2021/11/2021-ESG-Update_An-Integrated-Approach-to-ESG.pdf.

8. United Nations, Net-zero Coalition. https://www.un.org/en/climatechange/net-zero-coalition.

9. Energy & Climate Intelligence Unit, Net Zero Tracker. https://eciu.net/netzerotracker.

10. Black, R., Cullen, K., Fay, B., Hale, T., Lang, J., Mahmood, S., Smith, S.M. 2021. "Taking Stock: A global assessment of net zero targets." Energy & Climate Intelligence Unit and Oxford Net Zero. March, 2021. https://ca1-eci.edcdn.com/reports/ECIU-Oxford_Taking_Stock.pdf?mtime=20210323005817&focal=none.

11. CFA Institute, ESG Investing and Analysis. https://www.cfainstitute.org/en/research/esg-investing.

12. GRESB. "Partner: Green Building Initiative." https://gresb.com/nl-en/partners/green-building-initiative/.

13. Kamiya, George. 2021. "Data Centres and Data Transmission Networks." IEA. November, 2021. https://www.iea.org/reports/data-centres-and-data-transmission-networks.

14. Cyrus One. 2021. "2021 Sustainability Report." Cyrus One, 37. https://cyrusone.com/app/uploads/2021/11/2021-Sustainabilty-Report_Final.pdf.

About the Author

VICKI L. WORDEN

Vicki Worden is a sustainability thought leader and President and CEO of the Green Building Initiative (GBI), a nonprofit dedicated to making buildings healthy places to live and work while reducing their impacts on the environment.

Worden has dedicated her career to advancing environmental initiatives across North America. Her leadership has grown GBI into a thriving community supporting sustainability and wellness objectives in some of the world's largest real estate portfolios. She is a sought-after speaker, known trend-spotter and passionate, mission-based leader with special expertise in women's leadership in STEM, leveraging remote work structures and organizational change management.

Worden holds a BA in Political Science and International Relations from West Chester University of Pennsylvania, an MBA from Loyola University Maryland, and is a graduate of the U.S. Chamber of Commerce's Institute for Organizational Management. She lives in Camden, Maine, where she feeds her soul by hiking and skiing with her husband and dogs.

Learn more about the Green Building Initiative at thegbi.org, and connect with Worden on LinkedIn or via email at vworden@thegbi.org.

About Jaymie Scotto and Associates (JSA)

Jaymie Scotto & Associates (JSA) recognized a need for data centers and network infrastructure thought leaders to come together, share research, best practices and inspiration to support the industry as it makes greater strides towards achieving greener, more sustainable practices, technologies and facilities. With data consumption on an exponential rise, the need is now to define and provide timely blueprints and tools to reduce carbon emissions, enhance biodiversity, and harness the power in people and resource management. Out of this need, *Greener Data*, the multi-author book and industry-wide movement, was born.

Celebrating over 17 years of success, Jaymie Scotto & Associates (JSA) is the preeminent provider of Public Relations, Digital Marketing and Event Planning services to the telecom, data center and network infrastructure industries. Since its inception, JSA has also provided educational resources to these industries through a unique ecosystem of channels that include the JSA TV Video Newsroom, monthly c-level Virtual Roundtables, Telecom News Now Blog, JSA Podcasts including its popular *Data Movers* series, LinkedIn Live monthly news broadcasts and weekly industry e-newsletters.

Join the conversation with #GreenerData on LinkedIn and visit www.jsa.net to learn more.

About the Publisher

SOUL EXCELLENCE PUBLISHING

Soul Excellence Publishing is an independent hybrid publisher founded by Kayleigh O'Keefe. The publisher helps CEOs, founders, executives, and entrepreneurs turn their wisdom into culture-shaping books. Some of the company's international best-selling titles include:

- *Leading Through the Pandemic: Unconventional Wisdom from Heartfelt Leaders*
- *Significant Women: Leaders Reveal What Matters Most*
- *The X-Factor: The Spiritual Secrets Behind Successful Executives & Entrepreneurs*
- *STEM Century: It Takes a Village to Raise a 21st Century Graduate*
- *Black Utah: Stories from a Thriving Community*

A special thank you to the entire team who made the vision for this book a reality.

Website: https://soulexcellence.com/

Made in the USA
Las Vegas, NV
12 April 2022

47277210R00157